LIFE SCIENCE LIBRARY

THE BODY

LIFE SCIENCE LIBRARY

THE BODY

by Alan E. Nourse
and the Editors of **TIME-LIFE BOOKS**

Revised Edition

TIME-LIFE BOOKS ALEXANDRIA, VIRGINIA

CONTENTS

ABOUT THIS BOOK

THERE ARE MANY POSSIBLE APPROACHES to a study of the human body, but the most basic is to begin with an examination of how the body is constructed and how it functions. These two fundamentals form the theme of this book. The major organ systems of the body are explained in the light of the most recent discoveries of medical research.

The book contains both text chapters and picture essays. Each essay complements the chapter it follows, illustrating the subject in depth or adding to the information already supplied. Together, chapters and essays make up a unified whole, but each is self-contained and can be read independently. As an example: Chapter 3, "The Team of Bone and Muscle," is followed by an essay in which structural shapes found in engineering and architecture are matched with almost identical functional forms in the human skeleton.

THE AUTHOR

ALAN E. NOURSE, a practicing physician in North Bend, Washington, launched his writing career in order to help pay his way through the University of Pennsylvania Medical School, where he received his M.D. degree in 1951. Co-author of *Management of a Medical Practice*, he has also written *So You Want to Be a Doctor*, a guide for students contemplating a future in medicine. Another book by Dr. Nourse is *Nine Planets*, on the solar system, published in 1960.

ON THE COVER

The pliant strength of the human torso, evoked in a bronze by Auguste Rodin, is a quality of the body investigated throughout history by artist and scientist alike.

1
A Uniquely
Adaptable
Organism

"IN MY VIEW," wrote Thomas Jefferson in 1814, "no knowledge can be more satisfactory to a man than that of his own frame, its parts, their functions and actions." Distinguished thinkers before and since Jefferson have held this belief, but, curiously, it is not one which the average person wholeheartedly shares. Man's attitude toward his own body—his single most precious possession—is decidedly ambivalent. At one and the same time he is fascinated by it and fearful of it, partly in echo of ancient taboos, partly in the conviction that the body is too complicated to understand.

Rarely does man resolve this contradiction. What makes his body tick is both a subject of avid interest—sometimes too avid, as any doctor with hypochondriac patients can testify—and a matter of deliberate unconcern. Except in time of illness, the body itself encourages any tendency to ignore it. Normally, it demands little of its owner but food, clothing and shelter. Such vital functions as breathing and digestion proceed whether we heed them or not. Even when something breaks down, the body tries to repair the damage automatically.

The possible approaches to a study of the body are legion. To the cynic, the body is no more than a tenement of clay; to the poet, a palace of the soul; to the physician, an all-too-ailing hulk. The psychiatrist sees it as a housing for the mind and personality. The geneticist sees it as a perpetuator of its own kind. The biologist sees it as an organism which can alter the future as a result of the experience of the past. The anthropologist sees it as an accumulator of culture. Others have viewed the body as essentially just a machine, a concept that sometimes appeals and sometimes appalls. The English satirist, Samuel Butler, dismissed his fellow man as but "a pair of pincers set over a bellows and a stewpan and the whole thing fixed upon stilts." To the more reverent, the bodily mechanism is a masterpiece of precise planning, a delicate and complex apparatus whose various components work as a unit to achieve such diverse feats as scaling a mountaintop, building a bridge or composing a symphony.

All the specialized scientific views of the body are valid. All, however, must start from the same premise: an awareness of the body's basic structure and functions—its anatomy and physiology. This approach—the one which we shall take in these pages—is the broadest avenue to understanding. Used by investigators throughout history, it has led to most of what we know of the body today.

In this area of human knowledge, as in so many others, the 20th Century, with its remarkable new tools and techniques, has immeasurably added to our comprehension. Instruments have been devised to allow a direct look into the stomach's interior, or to excise a bit of bladder tissue for testing, or to extract fragments of liver or bone marrow for scrutiny.

THE HUMAN COMPLEX
From the beginning, the human body has provided a never-failing source of wonderment to its owner, to the artist celebrating its beauties, to the medical scientist probing its intricately meshed systems. As in other basic areas of knowledge, increased understanding of the body's structure and functions has led to an increased respect for its immense complexity.

Radioactive tracers, ingested into the body, help clarify complicated chemical reactions as they occur. X-ray diagnosis has become an art. In the 1970s computerized axial tomography (CAT) scanners combined X-rays with television cathode-ray tubes and computers to produce sophisticated cross-sectional views of the body once available only through surgery. Another new technique, diagnostic ultrasound, enables physicians to examine the body with high-frequency sound waves. The sound waves send back echoes that are transformed into pictures, in cross section, of the body's interior. These pictures provide a quick, painless and relatively inexpensive view into the body, one that is also far safer than radiation.

With these and myriad other devices, vital information about the body, hitherto unprovable, has been established: that the body is made up of an estimated 100 trillion cells; that these cells join to form basic types of tissue; that these tissues, in turn, are pieced together into complex organ systems; that the body thinks, moves, observes the world around it, enjoys pleasure and suffers pain only as a result of chemical reactions.

The triumph of a bridge

The sum total of what we know about the body to date represents a confluence of the work of doctor and scientist, of clinician as well as of researcher. Laboratory findings in physics, chemistry, physiology, microbiology, immunology and many other fields are ever more crucial to the physician. The results he obtains therefrom, in treating his patients, are essential to further research. So constant is the interchange that medicine, more effectively than any other discipline, has bridged the gap between art and science—the art of individual healing and the science of impersonal knowledge. The fusion was a long time coming. It has become incontrovertible fact only in our own day—a slow but inevitable result of the rise of the scientific method some 300 years ago.

Centuries before then, however, there were the precursors of today's doctors and scientists—the healers and the experimentalists. But the men who were more interested in making empirical deductions about the body per se were (and still are) far outnumbered by those more interested in tending to a particular person's health. Thus man's first knowledge of the body was largely compiled from specific case histories. Dealing with the body in disrepair, physicians of old drew innumerable conclusions about the body in health. Their judgments were often shallow or entirely in error, yet sometimes astonishingly accurate.

The Chinese promulgated all manner of rules for healthful living, such as regular exercise, avoidance of improperly cooked foods, and the use of mouthwash; no less a sage than Confucius himself cautioned, "Diseases enter by the mouth." The Hebrews—as any reader of the Old Testament will recall—laid down a doctrine of sanitation in food, water and bodily

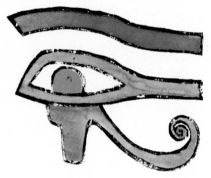

care that has persisted to this day. Probably the most knowing about the body among ancient peoples were the Egyptians. The Edwin Smith Papyrus, named for its 19th Century American discoverer and dated 1700 B.C., not only is the oldest surgical treatise extant but also reveals that the Egyptians recognized a relationship between the heart and blood vessels some 3,300 years before the great William Harvey issued his epochal verdict on the circulatory system. Archeologists have turned up clay tablets providing instruction to medical students and hieroglyphs depicting the stomach, liver, windpipe, spleen, bladder and womb. Even the specialist flourished: the inscription on one doctor's tomb labels him "Guardian of the Royal Bowel Movement." The Egyptians' main source of anatomical education was the embalming process. In preparing their dead to be mummified, they had to remove the more perishable parts of the body, such as the brain, lungs and intestines, to preserve the rest. X-rays of mummies have confirmed the deftness of these manipulations.

With the golden age of Greece in the Fifth Century B.C., individual personalities began to leave a deeper imprint upon medical annals. The first was Hippocrates, forever memorialized through the *Hippocratic Corpus*—the early Western world's bible of medical practice. How much of this collection of writings was his own, and how much the work of other men, can only be conjectured. Its wealth of lore ranged from guidance on cranial surgery and cataract operations to such minutiae as the faint noise given off by the chest when pleurisy was present—a sound like "the rubbing of leather." Theoretical and philosophical counsel was also offered. The physician should consult his colleagues when in doubt; he had a duty to record, with utter honesty, his failures as well as successes in treatment; above all, without love for mankind, he could have no love for the art of healing. The Hippocratic code of ethics is still taken as a solemn oath at medical school commencement exercises today.

An ego and its impact

The influence of the next towering figure in the history of medicine, Galen, lasted for some 1,400 years, from the height of his own prestigious career as physician to the Roman Emperor Marcus Aurelius during the Second Century A.D., until the late Middle Ages—indeed beyond, for his descriptions of the larger muscles of the body appear in medical textbooks to this day. A Greek from Asia Minor, Galen had a personality which brooked neither self-doubt nor outside criticism. One unfortunate effect of this egotism was the perpetuation of a number of bad guesses and unsupported theories, among them that "spirits" existed in the bloodstream, and that there were 27 varieties of pulse, including the wavelike, wormlike and antlike. But for all his misconceptions, Galen gave far greater precision to existing knowledge of anatomy and physi-

ANCIENT MEDICAL TEXT
An Egyptian papyrus of about 1700 B.C. indicates that physicians of the time knew something of anatomy. Hieroglyphs show such details as blood vessels emanating from the jug-shaped heart, although the symbol for bone is a structure like a coatrack. The symbols representing the brain include several phonetic signs. The papyrus dealt with injuries from head presumably to foot, although the surviving manuscript ends with the back.

HEART

BONE

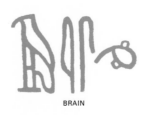

BRAIN

ology. His output of medical writing was phenomenal—more than 125 volumes, of which 83 still exist. They included treatises on the movement of muscles and on the intricate workings of nerves, and no fewer than 17 books on the uses of the various parts of the body.

With the restless new spirit of inquiry that began to pervade the Western world as the Renaissance approached, Galen's extended reign came to its end. His dethronement was bitterly fought; his teachings had both Church and academic blessing. Nevertheless, two men presumed to challenge his supremacy, and they prevailed.

Symbolic fire in a classroom

The first, Theophrastus Bombastus von Hohenheim, had all the swagger his middle name implied. Galen, at least, had acknowledged his debt to Hippocrates. This 16th Century Swiss healer deferred to no one. In fact, he is said to have chosen the name by which he is remembered—Paracelsus—to proclaim that he was superior even to Celsus, the great Roman encyclopedist. Paracelsus made a number of highly practical contributions to clinical medicine, among them one of the first studies of an occupational disease—the lung ailments of miners. But he left no less a legacy through a piece of brawling showmanship at the start of his teaching career at the University of Basel. Paracelsus launched his first lecture by setting fire to all the books by Galen he could find. This act symbolized the belief he bequeathed to all students of anatomy since: study the patient, rather than the textbooks, to learn about the body, for nothing supersedes the value of direct observation and experiment.

Andreas Vesalius of Belgium was only 13 when Paracelsus put Galen to the torch, but whether or not he heard of the deed he, too, concluded that Galen's ideas were imperfect. He studied medicine in Paris and then, at the improbable age of 23, was appointed a professor of anatomy at the University of Padua. By now dissection of the human cadaver—once banned as an impiety to the body—was no longer a rarity in medical classrooms. But those teachers who practiced it preferred merely to supply a running commentary, with pointer, as a hired barber-surgeon did the grubbing. Vesalius revolutionized this custom by performing his own dissections. He did them by the hundreds, and with such infinite pains that he was easily able to disprove many of Galen's assertions. After six years, he produced what has sometimes been called the greatest medical book ever written, *De Humani Corporis Fabrica* ("On the Fabric of the Human Body"). The first really accurate anatomy text, it was replete with minute detail and with brilliantly clear engravings by Stephen Calcar, a pupil of Titian. Some of them may be seen on pages 32 and 33.

After Paracelsus and Vesalius, the tempo of individual achievement in anatomy stepped up. It was a feat of pure technology, however, that pro-

THE MAN WHO PUT AN END TO MEDICINE-BY-FIRE

AMBROISE PARE'S DISCOVERY

The tools shown below are medieval instruments for cauterizing gunshot wounds. During the battle of Turin in 1537, French surgeon Ambroise Paré *(above)* ran out of cauterizing oil. He began to dress wounds with simple dressings. Later he noticed that patients responded to treatment more rapidly than did those whose wounds had been burned with hot oil. He vowed never again to cauterize wounded men.

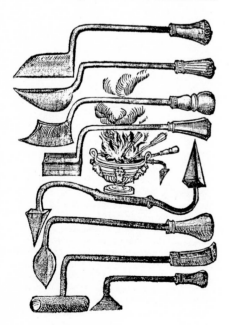

vided the next great threshold of exploration. The feat was the invention of the microscope. Thenceforth the study of anatomy became twofold. Gross anatomy dealt with what could be seen of the body with the unaided eye. Microscopic anatomy—now called histology—dealt with what had up to then been invisible and thus only speculative. Men could, at last, get to the nub of the matter: the cellular nature of all living things.

Simple magnifying lenses had been known as far back as the First Century A.D.; the Romans had used them to read and to start fires. But the microdimensional world around us could not begin to be fathomed until Hans and Zacharias Janssen, a father-and-son team of Dutch spectaclemakers, devised a microscope in 1590. As the first crude instruments gave way to finer models, they revealed an assortment of incredible wonders, most notably to the inquisitive eyes of Anton van Leeuwenhoek, a dry-goods clerk in Delft. Fascinated by the microscope's potential, Leeuwenhoek spent his off-duty hours scrutinizing through it any substance that came to hand—pond water, vinegar, milk, blood, bits of meat from between his teeth. All teemed with what he called "animalcules." Some, it turned out, were common bacteria. But he also delved into the world of the cell, ascertaining not only its existence but also its variety of size and shape. He found, for instance, that the red cells of the blood were shaped like disks, while the cells lining the inside of the mouth were shaped like old-fashioned bathroom-floor tiles.

Foibles of a correspondent

Leeuwenhoek imperishably endeared himself to later researchers by writing down everything he observed. Over the course of 50 years—from 1673 to his death in 1723—he bombarded the new Royal Society in London with more than 200 letters about his findings. They were laced with Leeuwenhoek's crotchety asides about the inanities of his neighbors and the state of his own health. But the august members of the Society recognized the diamond in the rough. As they increasingly relished the acuity of his scientific observations, Leeuwenhoek's fame spread. The purveyor of textile sundries even put on a command performance for Czar Peter the Great of Russia, regaling that autocrat with a microscopic peek at the capillary circulation in an eel's tail.

Leeuwenhoek's cell studies led to a wholly new concept of the makeup of all living organisms, including the human body. It did not dawn upon him, however, that the body might be made up *entirely* of cells. That remained to be confirmed a century later. In 1839 two Germans, Matthias Schleiden and Theodor Schwann, propounded the bedrock principle of our present understanding of the body: that all living matter is composed of cells basically similar in structure and function.

Subsequent studies of the cell—what it is, what it does and how it

A MAN OF MAGIC AND MEDICINE
Theophrastus Bombastus von Hohenheim, better known as Paracelsus, was the 16th Century Swiss physician who pioneered in the use of several modern medical techniques. Although he was also engrossed with the occult arts, Paracelsus is credited as the father of anesthesia; he wrote "Miners' Sickness," the first treatise on occupational diseases, and he insisted on cleanliness as a vital necessity for health.

reproduces itself—have revealed it to be a fantastically complex world in itself. For the purposes of this book, only certain fundamental facts about it need be stated here. One of the major wonders of the cell is the disparity between its minuteness and the prodigiousness of its activity. Each cell is so tiny that millions of them may be found in a half-inch cube of human body tissue. Yet each comprises an almost unimaginably busy chemical laboratory with a highly ordered division of labor.

A swarm of tiny specialists

The cell has two main parts: a nucleus, containing the genetic material deoxyribonucleic acid (DNA), and a surrounding semifluid cytoplasm. Bounding the cytoplasm is the cell membrane, which keeps the cell contents in and undesirable material out, yet permits passage of both proper nutrients and wastes. The nucleus—cell headquarters—governs the major activities of the cytoplasm; its finest hour, however, comes at reproduction time, when chromosomes containing DNA split. It is in the cytoplasm that the cell's day-to-day business is carried on. Each of its various components, or organelles, is a specialist of surpassing skill. One type breaks down the food given entry by the cell membrane and converts it into energy. Another provides the site for the synthesis of protein —along with reproduction, a major function of most cells. Another packages the manufactured protein for transport wherever needed in the body.

To operate efficiently, the cell thus requires specific help from the body as a whole: food to provide raw material for the release of energy, oxygen to help break down the food, water to transport inorganic substances like calcium and sodium. Once its needs are satisfied, the cell itself provides the intricate mechanism for maintaining the balance essential to keep it in kilter—in short, to keep the body alive and healthy.

Cells share certain common characteristics, but most of the body's cells develop specialized features and abilities. The cells that form bone collect calcium salts; these cells are locked together in solid chunks, immobile. By contrast, the white cells of the blood, which fight off invading bacteria, roam freely about the body. Other cells make special chemicals for the body's use—the hormones produced in the endocrine glands, or the digestive enzymes poured into the intestine from the pancreas. Still other cells form the incredibly thin membranes in the lung or kidney that permit the filtering or exchange of dissolved body fuels and wastes.

According to their particular features and their intended functions, cells form different types of tissue: bone, muscle, blood, nerve tissue, connective tissue and epithelium. The cells that make up each of these are not identical, but belong together by reason of underlying similarities.

For example, the cells of bowel muscle are rounder and shorter than the long, spindly cells of leg muscle, yet both kinds contract forcefully when stimulated by a chemical or electrical impulse. The cells that make up bone tissue differ sufficiently to make brittle bone in one place and spongy, resilient cartilage in another, yet all store the salts which give bone its calcified structure. The loose network of cells that supports the fatty padding under the skin and the dense capsule of cells that holds the knee joint in place are both forms of connective tissue. All nerve cells, varied as they may be, receive and conduct electrochemical impulses. All blood cells, varied as they may be, float freely in a circulating fluid, plasma.

The most versatile cells are those of the various kinds of epithelium. Forming the body's external coating—the skin—epithelial cells protect things inside from things outside. They also form the lining of the mouth, stomach and bowel, the inner surface of blood vessels, and the membranes that permit the lungs to breathe and the kidneys to excrete. Over the cornea of the eye they become a sort of transparent windshield, to permit the free entry of light to the retina. Other epithelial cells secrete a protective mucus to keep intestines, lungs and nasal passages from drying out. Still others manufacture powerful hormones that regulate the body's chemical reactions.

Interlock and overlap

The tissues comprise the structural materials of the body's organ systems. These, in turn, may be compared to a number of corporations with interlocking directorates. Indeed the interdependence of the organ systems has led to some disagreement over how many there are. The venerable *Gray's Anatomy*—used by medical students for more than 100 years—lists 10 systems: nervous, digestive, respiratory, vascular, urogenital, endocrine, skeletal, muscular, joints and external covering. Other authorities categorize joints and bones together because they are so closely related, or separate the sense organs from the nervous system, or lump all the internal organs—respiratory, digestive, endocrine and urogenital— under the resounding title of splanchnological system.

Far more important than their labels is the fact that the systems interact; the breakdown of one can damage or destroy the others. Ideally, of course, all systems would do their jobs perfectly all the time. Unfortunately, nature permits no such perfection. All of them suffer from malfunctions at one point or another. The wonder is that breakdowns are the exception rather than the rule.

Within the healthy body itself there is no absolute criterion for "normal." Variations occur not only between individuals, but within the individual himself, sometimes from hour to hour, depending on his activity at the time. Doctors privately joke that even a baboon could get through medical school if he learned to say, with enough profundity, "It varies." One of the practitioner's major headaches is to determine whether a pa-

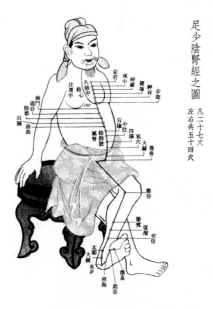

CHINESE MEDICAL CHART
This Ming Dynasty (14th to 17th Century) drawing is, according to the archaic Chinese characters, a chart for curing kidney ailments. The vertical line plotted on the patient was believed to relate to the kidney; the cure consisted of jabbing it with needles in the 27 places indicated. Called acupuncture, the ancient art of pricking the ill with very thin needles has attracted the attention of Western doctors. In addition to its use as therapy, acupuncture can be employed as an analgesic during surgery, replacing anesthesia. A scientific understanding of acupuncture and its effectiveness is not yet fully realized.

tient's condition reflects an actual illness or merely a variation within a broad range of normal. The breadth of this range may be indicated by a few statistics. The weight of the healthy heart is considered to be anywhere between 240 and 360 grams; the weight of the healthy liver, between 1,000 and 2,000 grams; the level of sugar in the blood, between 70 and 130 milligrams.

Aside from the range of normal, another remarkable aspect of the body is its range of strength and weakness. It can survive in blast-furnace desert heat by adjusting its built-in heating system, yet an internal temperature eight degrees above the normal range of 97° to 99° F. (36° to 37° C.) may destroy vital nervous tissue. A man can draw enough food from stored fat to stay alive for weeks (if he has water), but would die in about five minutes if the oxygen supply to all his cells were cut off by a failure in breathing. An Olympics champion has lifted as much as 975½ pounds (442½ kg), deadweight, yet a vacation-bound executive lifting a heavy suitcase may bring on the agony of a "slipped disk" in his spine.

The human body has no corner on such strengths and weaknesses; they are shared by all mammals. The uniqueness of man's strength, perhaps, lies in the fact that his body was not built for just one or two specialized purposes, but is marvelously adaptable. That he is so unspecialized, indeed, may account for his dominance among the species on this planet.

Changing Views of the Body

From prehistoric times until the mid-16th Century, when the findings of the physician-teacher Vesalius established the principle of firsthand observation, the body was seen less as a biological organization than as a house for the spirit. The scientific study of the human body is in fact a relatively recent development. The ancients rooted their studies in the butchery of animals at the altar and in the kitchen, but investigations were fettered by superstition, religion and tradition. Nevertheless, the exigencies of everyday life—on the battlefield, in the sickroom—demanded that wounds be healed and ailments cured. Thus, driven by the need to doctor diseases of every kind, men learned the chief parts of the body, devised names for them and evolved theories to account for their miraculous operation. These theories, although ultimately replaced by more useful concepts, were defended with a faith which it took a Renaissance to dislodge.

A 15TH CENTURY ANATOMY CLASS
Perched in a pulpit, a red-robed professor of anatomy delivers the gospel according to Galen, a Second Century Greek physician whose theories, based on the observation of animals, animated medicine for 1,400 years. An assistant *(far right)* points out parts of the body while a barber-surgeon dissects the cadaver. If actual observations conflicted with Galen, they were discarded.

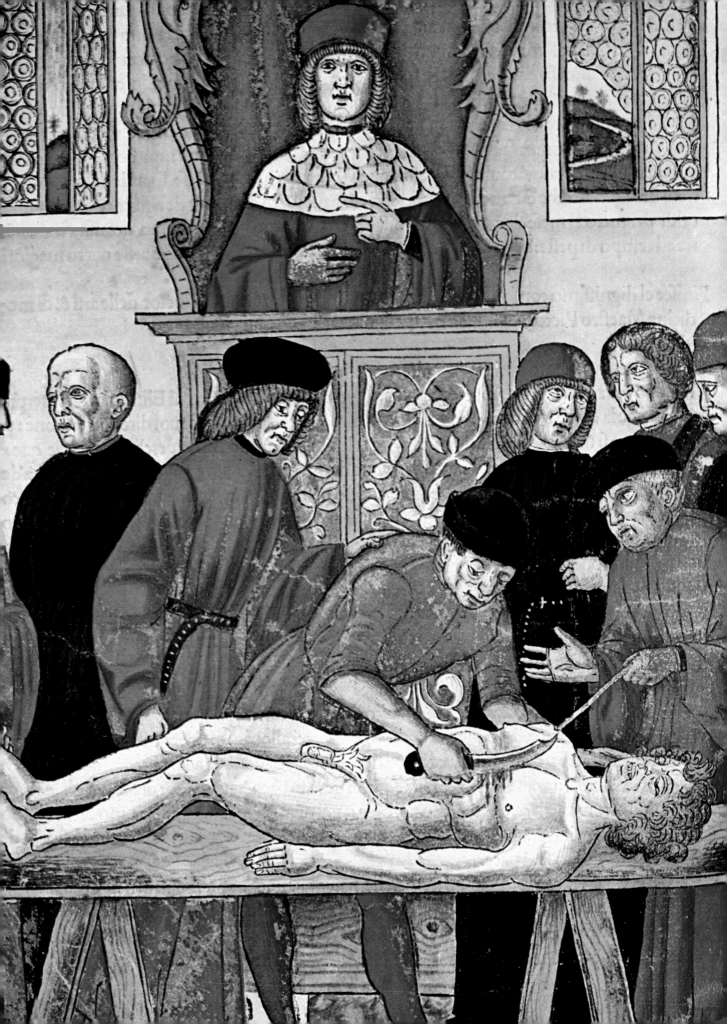

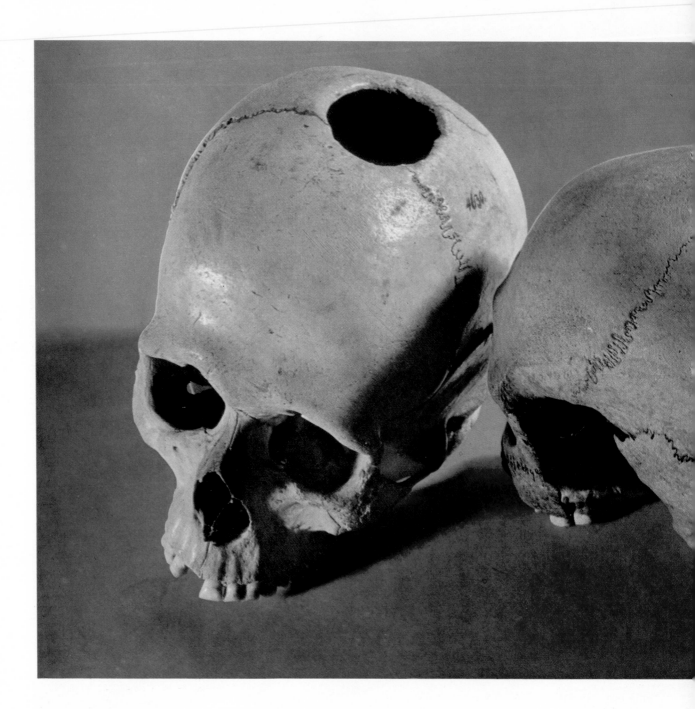

Primitive Surgeons
of the Skull

Guided by empirical observations and magical beliefs but armed with little more than sharpened flints, Cro-Magnon "surgeons" learned about the body while treating diseases, setting broken bones and caring for wounds.

The most spectacular practice of the era was trephination, the surgical exposure of the brain to permit the flight of "spirits" from the heads of persons suffering from fractures, epilepsy, migraine, melancholia and paralysis. These trephined skulls have been found among the remains of primitive peoples around the world.

The operation consisted of opening the scalp to uncover the cranial bone, cutting out a round *(above)* or square piece of bone *(right)*, cleansing and dressing the opening and, finally, replacing the scalp flap. Since the skull is generally insensitive to pain, especially on the top, no drugs were needed to anesthetize the patient during the operation—which took anywhere from 30 minutes to several hours to perform. The presence of new bone growth around the incisions *(above right)* indicates the remarkable fact that about half the patients survived.

AN ORNATE SURGICAL KNIFE
The sculpted scene on the handle-tip of this Peruvian *tumi,* or trephining knife, shows how the operation was performed. The patient is held as the surgeon scrapes through to the bone with his bronze scalpel. This instrument was designed for cross-hatched cuts like those shown below.

VICTIM AND SURVIVOR
Two Paleolithic skulls *(above)* from Denmark reveal healed and unhealed trephined openings. The skull at right shows how new growth began at the edges and filled in much of the opening. The skull at left indicates the patient died before the bone had time to grow again.

A PAIR OF WINDOWS ON THE BRAIN
Cross-hatch trephination, achieved by intersecting straight cuts *(right),* was performed in Peru some 12,000 years ago. Survival depended on the location of the boring. If it touched on the sagittal suture—the midline at the top of the skull—fatal hemorrhaging often occurred.

An Early Contribution from Religion

Egyptian religion at the time of the early pharaohs might have served as a fruitful source of anatomical knowledge, for through the sacred ritual of embalming the dead the Egyptians evolved an extensive medical vocabulary and wrote the first medical texts. However, embalming was a process of preservation, not a discipline for studying the structure of the body. As a consequence, organs were carelessly removed and dissections for the sake of knowledge were not performed. Nevertheless, the effects —if not the causes—of injuries and diseases were noted, and experiments in surgery and pharmacy were conducted. Egyptian physicians learned to use splints and bandages with skill, and their remedies became famous.

AN ANTIDOTE FOR POISONS
A granite statue of the healer-priest Dje-Mer, sculpted in 320 B.C. *(above),* is covered with magical inscriptions to combat scorpion stings and snake bites. Water poured over the statue accumulated in a small depression at its base and, when drunk, supposedly effected a cure.

PREPARATIONS FOR A JOURNEY
This mummification scene *(opposite)* on the coffin of the priest Zed-Bastet-Fesanch shows (reading from bottom to top) two priests cleansing and anointing the body; a procession led by the jackal-headed god Anubis, at the bier; Anubis mummifying the body and placing it on another bier above jars containing entrails; offerings at the shrine where the entrails are kept.

A UNIVERSAL EGYPTIAN REMEDY
In this painted relief, a tiny physician dispenses beer to his lordly patient. Beer was frequently used to administer drugs orally. And the lees, or dregs, of beer were themselves important emollients prescribed for digestive disorders and for boils. In our own time, it has been discovered that these dregs are a source of vitamin B and a number of valuable antibiotic substances.

CURE FOR A WOUNDED HERO

A fresco from Pompeii depicts a scene from Virgil's *Aeneid* in which the hero Aeneas, supported by his spear and his son Julius, is treated by the physician, Iapix. Venus, Aeneas' mother-goddess, appears with a medicinal herb which will stop the flow of blood and ease the pain.

An Enlightened Look at the Body

The physician-naturalists of ancient Greece viewed the human body as a subject for dispassionate study unconditioned by superstitions. Clinical observations led physicians like Hippocrates in the Fifth Century B.C. to conceive of the body as a grouping of interrelated parts, and illness as a malfunction of one or more of these parts. Such precedents paved the way for the great anatomical researches of Galen, a Second Century Greek physician who practiced in Rome. Galen's work describing his examinations of human bones and animal viscera became the bible of anatomists for the next 1,400 years.

CLUES IN AN ANIMAL'S ENTRAILS
This Etruscan bronze model of a sheep's liver from the Third Century B.C. is inscribed with the names of 47 divinities believed to cause sickness in humans. Discovering real or imagined peculiarities in livers of sacrificed sheep was a popular Roman diagnostic technique.

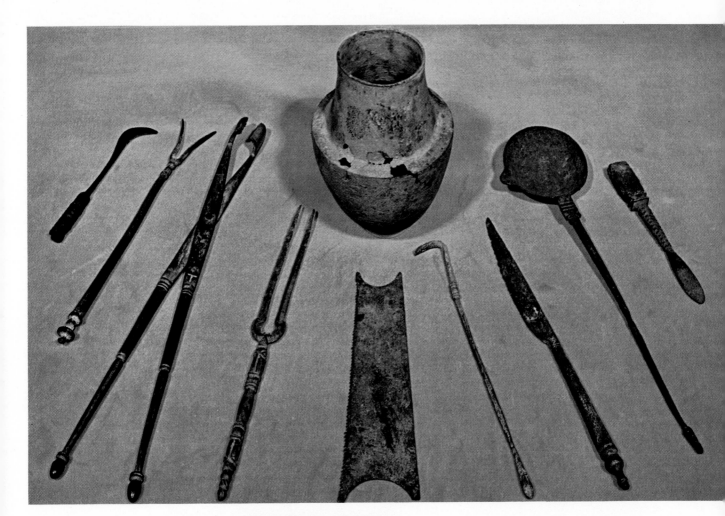

AN ANCIENT DOCTOR'S TOOLS
Roman surgical instruments include *(from left to right)* a scalpel handle for steel blades, an arrowhead retractor, forceps, another retractor, a surgical saw, a hook for tissue excision, a scalpel, a spoon for warming salves and another scalpel handle. In the center is a bleeding cup.

Fanciful Figures in Medieval Anatomy

During the Middle Ages, knowledge of anatomy and the various body systems was derived almost exclusively from the works of Galen, which were not illustrated. The quartet of bizarre bodies below, for example, was appended to a 13th Century English medical manuscript and was thought to represent Galen's ideas of the body's inner structures. These primitive drawings may have been inspired by an Arabic book, like the one opposite, or they may have been the renderings of an imaginative artist. In either case, the text itself was rooted in Galen. He originally wrote in Greek and, over the centuries, was translated from Greek to Arabic and, from the 11th Century on, from Arabic into Latin.

Despite the misconceptions of the original and the embellishments of countless translators, few dared to question Galen's authority. Even when human dissections began to gain acceptance, their sole intention was to verify Galen's observations. In the gross distortions below, undersized lungs are joined, upper ribs are completely absent, the nervous system does not include the brain and the esophagus leads to the heart.

Drawings from a medieval manuscript show (from left to right) concepts of the major human organs plus the muscular system; the skeleta

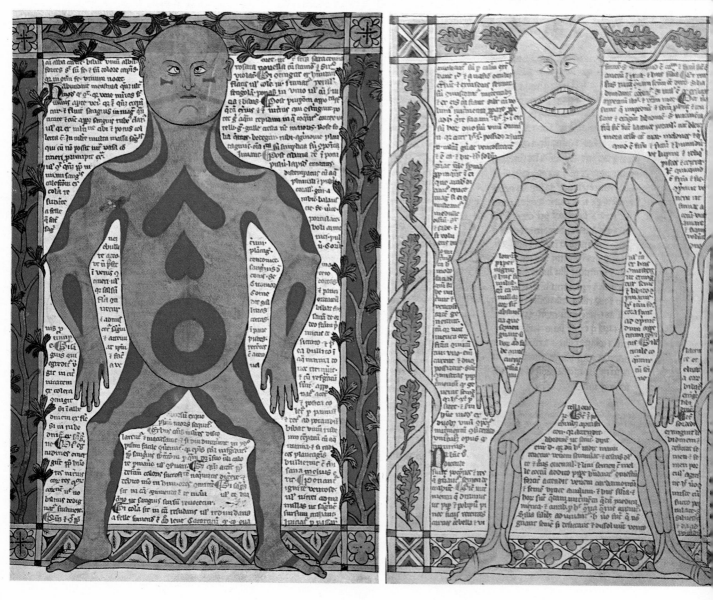

A CLASSIC TREATISE
The *Canon of Medicine* by the Persian, ibn Sina, or Avicenna (980-1037), greatest physician-scholar of his day, is based on Arabic versions of Galen. On the right-hand page is a drawing of Avicenna lecturing to students; on the left, a rendering of the body similar to those shown below. Avicenna's anatomical works were the most widely read in Europe in the late Middle Ages.

tructure; the nervous and circulatory systems. The crude sketches failed to emphasize Galen's belief in the importance of the liver.

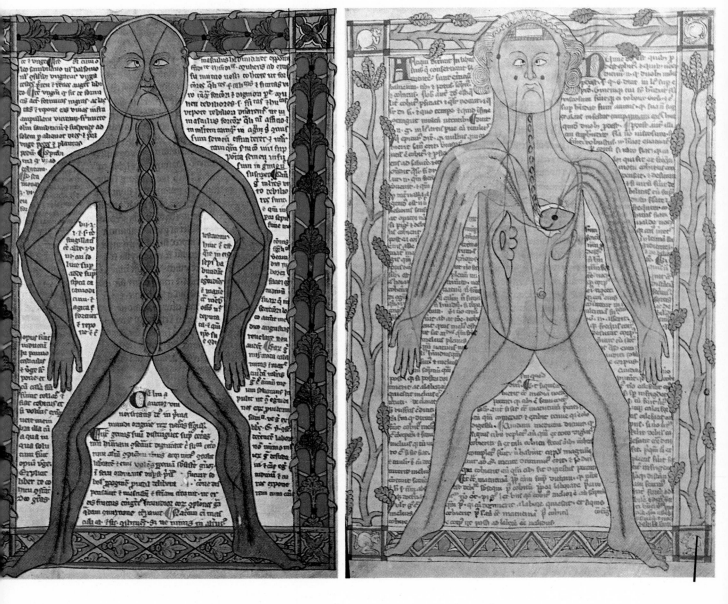

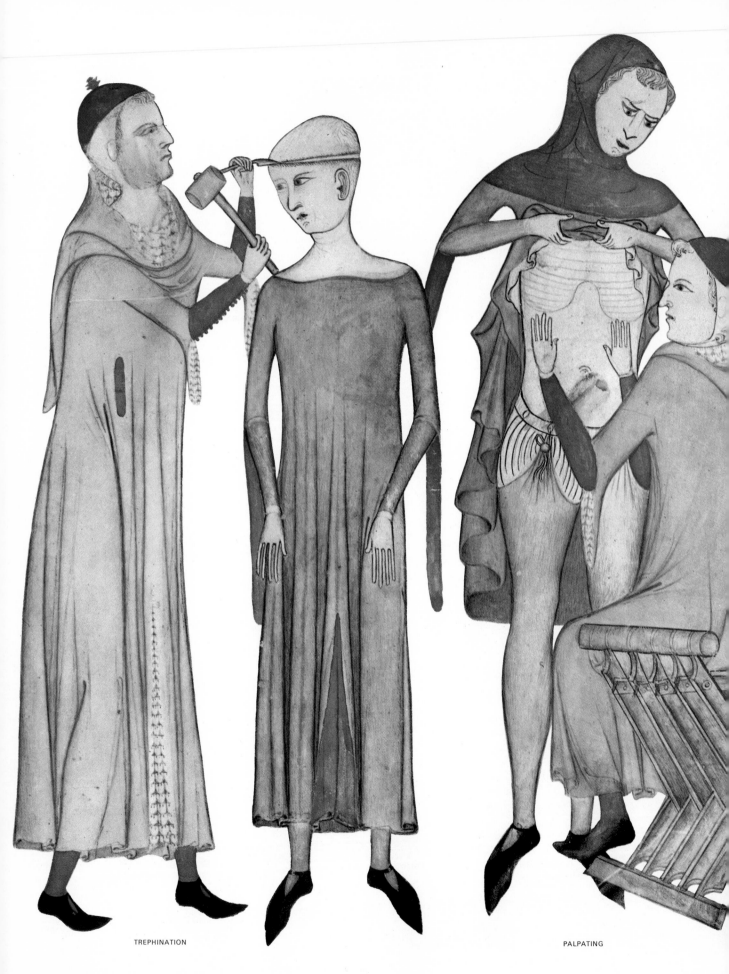

TREPHINATION

PALPATING

Medieval Sense and Nonsense

To the doctors of the Middle Ages, common sense in dealing with the human body was a quality that usually yielded to uncommon faith and a reliance on tradition. Consequently, they often employed accurate diagnostic techniques for ailments that they then treated with irrelevant, even fatal, cures based on ancient theories.

For example, physicians like those shown here were able to arrive at a primitive estimate of body temperatures and of pathological changes in the spleen and liver by palpating, or feeling, the chest and abdomen *(center)*. Or, in taking the pulse *(right)*, they could feel the arterial pressure and the flexibility of the blood-vessel walls. But because they believed that an imbalance of four body fluids, called humors, led to disease, these physicians frequently ended up applying dangerous remedies. Two of them, bloodletting and trephination *(far left)*, had originated in antiquity.

DIAGNOSIS AND "CURE"
Drawings from the pages of an illuminated manuscript on anatomy written by Guido da Vigevano, a physician to Philip VI of France in the middle 1300s, show an operation to open the skull and two types of physical examinations. By this time the Church had prohibited clergymen from practicing medicine, for it took up too much of their time. Thus, medicine was secularized; the practice passed to barber-surgeons and the theory to university-trained physicians.

PULSE-TAKING

A Spate of Bizarre Remedies

The apothecaries of the Middle Ages and Renaissance viewed the human body as an experimental laboratory in which almost any substance could be tested in the hope of finding cures for almost everything. In a very real sense, their customers were the guinea pigs of the day, and often failed to survive the treatment.

As late as the 16th Century, European pharmacy was still based on the work of Dioscorides. A Greek surgeon and naturalist of the First Century, he compiled the knowledge of plant remedies handed down by the Egyptians, Greeks and Romans. His and other compilations were known as herbals. They included both sound suggestions, such as poppy juice to kill pain (poppies were known to contain a narcotic, now identified as opium), and seemingly inane ideas, such as the use of strawberry roots for mad-dog bites and oats for impetigo. Minerals too were used to assault the ailing body, as were animal fat, marrow and bones. Crocodile blood was recommended for failing eyesight.

Often apothecaries diagnosed diseases to sell a certain plant cure. Actually they had little knowledge of medicine. Indeed, until the 14th Century, apothecaries were grocers who carried medicines as a sideline.

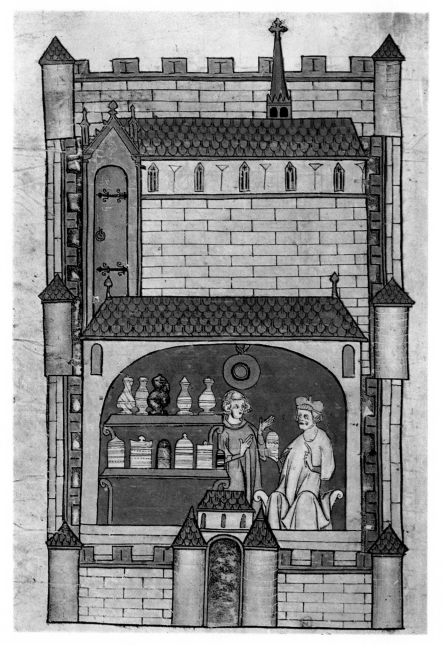

AZTEC PLANT TO TREAT PELVIC DISORDERS

AZTEC MEDICINAL PLANT DESCRIBED IN 1552

AN APOTHECARY SHOP
An illumination from a 13th Century manuscript shows an apothecary and customer. Apothecaries gathered herbs and prepared thousands of supposed remedies. Sometimes one prescription contained a hundred or more drugs, some of which came from as far away as the New World.

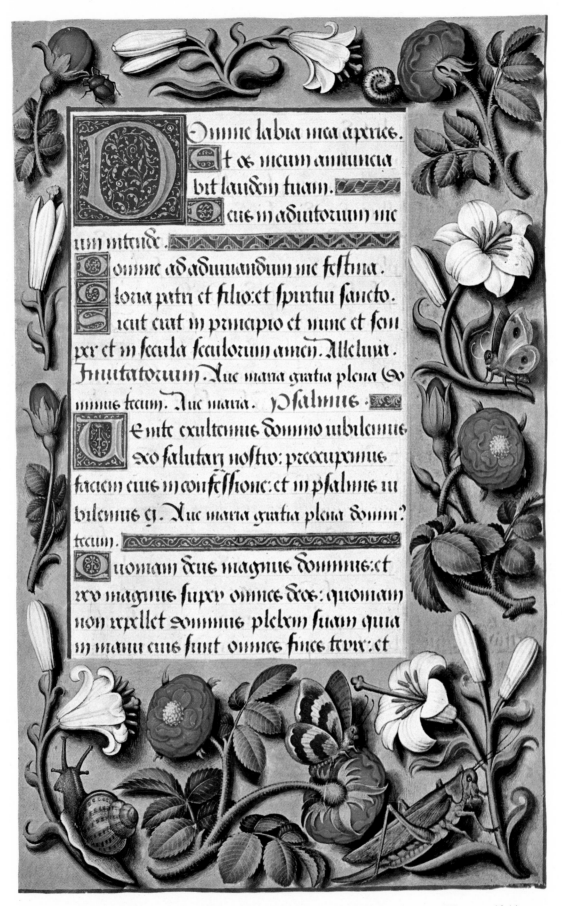

The illuminations in a 1505 prayer book show roses, used for eye and heart disorders, and lilies, used for burns.

Harassing the Body's Humors

Since the cause of disease was considered by the Greeks to be morbid influences on the body's humors—blood, phlegm, black bile and yellow bile—it followed that many illnesses could be diagnosed by examining the body's discharges and treated by allowing the ostensibly infected fluids to escape. By the end of the 15th Century this logic had made uroscopy the chief form of diagnosis and elevated bloodletting to the status of a universal treatment. So fashionable were they that physicians amassed fortunes in their application.

Doctors like those at left would examine vials of urine to determine its color, odor, density and content. The sediment in a urine sample was thought to be made up of four layers, each of which corresponded to a region of the body. Cloudiness of the top layer, for example, was supposed to indicate a disease of the head; of the bottom layer, a bladder disorder, and so on. The usual cure for these and other ailments was bleeding. Much controversy was generated around how much blood should be taken, when, and how near or distant from the affliction the incision should be made. Thus the Italian poet Petrarch could quote Pliny condemning physicians who, "to make a name for themselves through some novelty . . . traffic with our lives."

THE PHYSICIANS' OFFICE
An illuminated drawing from a manuscript executed at Bruges around 1482 depicts a pair of patients waiting for treatment outside an office shared by two physicians; inside, the richly clad colleagues are taking blood from one patient's arm and examining the urine of another. Frequently leeches were used instead of a knife to "suck" humors from a diseased area.

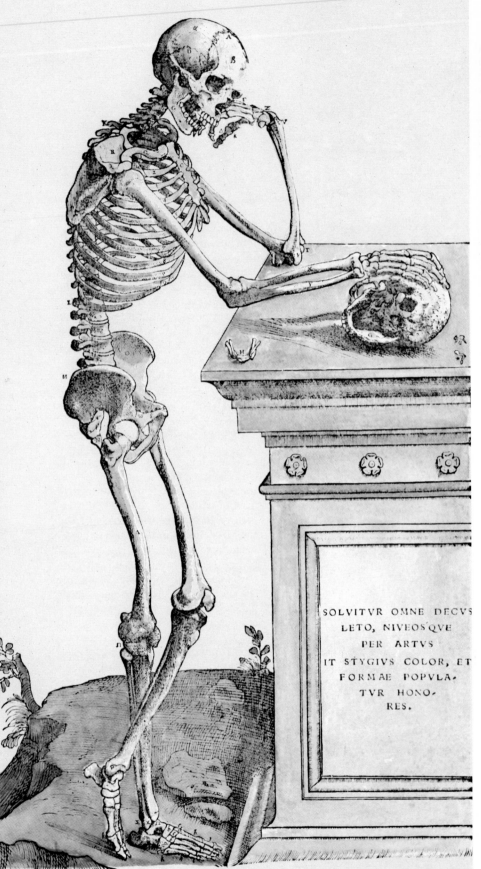

SOLVITVR OMNE DECVS
LETO, NIVEOSQVE
PER ARTVS
IT STYGIVS COLOR, ET
FORMAE POPVLA-
TVR HONO-
RES.

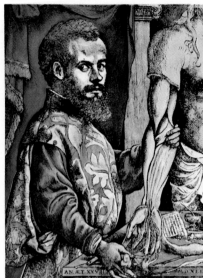

PORTRAIT OF VESALIUS BY CALCAR

The Beginning of Modern Anatomy

In 1543, the year the Flemish-born anatomist Andreas Vesalius first published his controversial epic, *De Humani Corporis Fabrica*, the dictum, "It is more right to err with Galen than be right with others," was finally and irrevocably discredited. Vesalius, who taught at the University of Padua, was only 29 years old when he introduced a systematic anatomy founded not on faith and analogies from animal anatomy but on studies of original dissections of the human cadaver.

De Fabrica, which is still a basically accurate guide to bones and joints, muscles, the vascular and nervous systems, viscera, heart, lungs and brain, was exquisitely illustrated by Stephen Calcar, two of whose woodcuts are reproduced on these pages.

A THOUGHTFUL SKELETON
A woodcut *(left)* from *De Fabrica* shows a skeleton meditating over a skull. Posing these figures in lifelike positions was characteristic of Calcar, who worked under Vesalius' direct supervision.

A FLAYED BODY
A figure from *De Fabrica* looks out over authentic countryside near Padua. If the backgrounds to these muscle illustrations are placed in a sequence, they will form a continuous landscape.

VNDECIMA
MVSCVLO,
RVM TA,
BVLA,

2
Hallmarks of Individual Identity

AN ESTIMATED FOUR BILLION HUMAN BEINGS inhabit the earth, yet not one exactly duplicates another. This is a fact most people would find difficult to believe. Occidentals often cannot distinguish between Orientals, an inability which Orientals reciprocate. Even within one's own race, the conviction persists that each man has his exact double, somehow, somewhere.

Strong resemblances of face and figure do, indeed, exist. Often they are striking enough to provide a tyrant or other potential human target with an effective stand-in. In one historic case in World War II records, an Australian actor posing as Field Marshal Montgomery visited North Africa before D-Day and filled the part so well that German agents promptly discounted the imminence of a Normandy invasion. Had the British military leader and his impersonator stood side by side, however, the differences between them would have been easily apparent. Even so-called identical twins have their dissimilarities, however minute.

One of the most remarkable features of the human body, in short, is its individuality of appearance. The odds would seem to be overwhelmingly against such uniqueness. The relatively few major components of the human exterior should, in theory at least, diversify in only limited ways. On the contrary, they form an infinity of variations on the same theme. Each man's shell is his own personal ensign, clearly setting him apart from any other human being in the present or past.

Heredity, environment and human experience all do their share in fashioning the physical differences which we present to the world. The influence of these factors is so intertwined that no scientist has yet been able to say, with certainty, where one leaves off and the other begins. The size of the body, for example, is in part determined by skeletal structure, which is largely a matter of family and racial inheritance. But size may also be vitally affected by environmental conditions, notably those which provide adequate nutrition and freedom from disease, and by a hormone that is called somatotropin. This substance, named from the Greek for "body-nourishing," is secreted by the front lobe of the pituitary gland, at the base of the skull, and is essential for normal growth. A shortage of somatotropin during youth, when bones have not yet reached maturity, will stunt the body.

Perhaps the most curious fact about the human exterior is the tendency of most people to dissociate it from matters of bodily health, to regard it as simply a front behind which the business of well-being is independently conducted. More often than not, their chief concern with this façade is to adorn it. Indeed, statistics show that Americans spend more money for cosmetics than the federal government's National Institutes of Health provide in grants for medical research. In one year, for example, Americans lavished $681,700,000 on lipsticks alone, $456,120,000 on face

THE STAMP OF ORIGINALITY
Laced with wrinkles and sagging with folds of flesh, the toilworn face of this Tennessee woman at the age of 77 seems at first glance to be indistinguishable from those of legions of other oldsters. But as with every other individual, her features reflect a particular confluence of hereditary and environmental factors that bestows the gift of uniqueness upon every human exterior.

creams and $410,820,000 on hair-coloring preparations. They also paid out $164,300,000 for reducing aids.

(The scope of human vanity is, of course, far from a new story. In 1770 an Englishman who may have been soured by personal experience introduced into Parliament a bill which revealed the wide range of surface attractions employed by the women of the realm. He proposed to pin a witchcraft charge on any of them—"of whatever age, rank, profession, or degree, whether virgins, maids, or widows"—who lured one of His Majesty's subjects into matrimony by the use of "scents, paints, cosmetic washes, artificial teeth, false hair, Spanish wool, iron stays, hoops, high heeled shoes, bolstered hips.")

Signals from a showcase

While no doctor would dispute the importance of a reasonable amount of pride in self-appearance, the outer covering of the body—the so-called cutaneous system—serves a number of purposes far more sober than that of mere showcase. It is, to begin with, the most obvious indicator of an individual's general condition. Among the more apparent indexes are flabbiness, an overabundance of fat or a notable scarcity of it. But to the physician's practiced eye there are many other manifestations of health, or the lack of it, in the skin and in its related structures, the hair and nails. The skin alone provides many warning signals. Its texture may reflect a nutritional deficiency or a malfunction of the glands. A flush may indicate the presence of fever. A rash or other eruption may herald one of many common infections. Coarsening and wrinkling furnish clues that aging is taking place.

The skin, however, not only mirrors but also actively contributes to bodily health. It is as much a vital organ as the heart, liver or lungs and, like each of them, has its own special responsibilities:

• It is a nearly waterproof container, enclosing the body's content, 60 per cent of which is fluid, and preventing it from drying out.

• It is a receptor, housing nerve endings which receive sensory stimuli from the environment.

• It is both a radiator and retainer of heat, serving as an insulator and helping maintain the body's temperature at a constant level.

• It is a barrier, guarding the body against external injury and intruding toxic chemicals.

• It is an inhibitor, producing acids that prevent the growth of bacteria and fungus.

The skin is endowed with double insurance against a breakdown in these crucial functions. First, it has a remarkable ability to regenerate itself. When wounded, it responds with an immediate proliferation of new skin cells; so thoroughgoing is the healing process that when, for example,

THE TELLTALE RIDGES OF SKIN
Of all the body's external characteristics, the most distinctive, and perhaps the least noticed, are the ridges of skin covering the fingertips. Well provided with sweat pores, these ridges almost always leave uniquely convoluted marks—fingerprints—whenever an object is touched. The individuality of any fingerprint has been established beyond doubt; of more than 170 million now on file with the FBI, no two are so similar that an expert cannot readily tell them apart. Fingerprinting as a positive means of identification gave criminology a higher degree of precision. Eight basic types of prints are shown below.

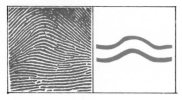

PLAIN ARCH

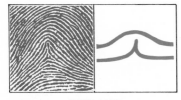

TENTED ARCH

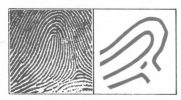

RADIAL LOOP (RIGHT HAND)

ULNAR LOOP (RIGHT HAND)

PLAIN WHORL

a fingertip is injured, even the fingerprint whorls will be restored to their previous, unique pattern. Second, the skin can respond well to an emergency created by damage so severe that the full thickness of the skin is destroyed, as happens in the case of a third-degree burn. In most cases it proves strikingly receptive to a graft of a thin layer of skin that is taken from another part of the body. Usually applied to the burned area in little squares about the size of postage stamps, the transplanted skin eventually adapts to its new site, growing more skin out from its edges until the patches all come together. Meanwhile, skin surrounding the donor site regenerates on its own.

The skin is at no point more than about one fifth of an inch (6 mm) thick—testimony enough to the truth of the term "skin-deep." But for all its shallowness, it is a marvelously intricate structure, composed of layer upon layer—each with its own reason for being.

The versatile epidermis

The epidermis, or outer part of the skin (literally, "the skin upon"), is composed of two to four layers, and varies in thickness from 0.06 inch (1.4 mm) to 0.003 inch (0.07 mm). The top layer, the *stratum corneum*, is made up of a tough mass of dead cells that are continuously being shed by the body. A brisk toweling of the skin is enough to rub off a fair sampling of this outer layer, whose cells contain keratin, a fibrous, horny substance that at the tips of the fingers and toes becomes the protective nails. The epidermis is self-renewing. Cells produced in its bottom layer, the *stratum germinativum*, constantly push upward to replace the dead and dying cells topside.

In addition to its function as cell-restorer, the *stratum germinativum* plays another key role. It is the main home of the melanocytes, cells which produce melanin, the pigment responsible for skin color. The varieties of skin color in mankind result from varieties in the distribution and quantity of melanin in the skin. The melanocytes of the fair-complexioned, for example, contain only a few granules of melanin, while those of the dark-skinned are crowded with it. Melanin helps protect the skin from the ultraviolet radiation of the sun; thus people in sunnier climates have darker skin than those in areas which receive less sunlight. Those with fair skin are most susceptible to the harmful effects of the sun's radiation and are easily sunburned; excessive and frequent exposure to ultraviolet radiation can cause skin cancer.

Determining skin color is only one function of the melanocytes. Other melanocytes located in the hair and the iris of the eye produce the pigment that governs hair and eye color. The melanocytes of the brown-eyed contain more melanin than those of the blue-eyed; in the hair, graying signals a stoppage in melanin production.

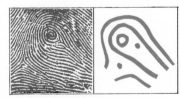

CENTRAL POCKET LOOP

DOUBLE LOOP

ACCIDENTAL

Beneath the epidermis is the dermis, or inner part of the skin. It is the thickest part of the skin, ranging from one fifth of an inch (6 mm) at the soles of the feet to less than two hundredths of an inch (0.5 mm) at the eyelids. It too is composed of several layers.

One of the primary functions of the skin—both dermis and epidermis—is to guard the body against abrasive and destructive forces in the surrounding environment, and in doing so it invokes a variety of stratagems. To shield the cornea of the eye, it provides the delicate outer covering of the eyelid. To counter wear and tear on pressure points such as the palms of the hands and soles of the feet, it thickens into callus. On the fingertips, to provide the necessary traction and grip, it forms tiny ridges similar to the treads on an automobile tire. Over the knuckles, elbows and knees it is pleated to allow flexibility of the joints.

The scrawny and the stout

Below the dermis lies a webbing of fibrous tissue, the subcutaneous fascia (literally, "bundles under the skin"), which is the last barrier between the skin and the interior of the body. Within these areas are contained the nerve endings, the smallest blood vessels, the roots of the hair, the sweat glands, the sebaceous, or oil-producing, glands which help give the skin its softness and pliancy, and the globules of fat which, depending on the amount that has been accumulated, give us appearances described as scrawny, sylphlike or stout.

Even as the outer part of the skin provides external protection for the body, the inner part also has its specialized functions to perform. Although widely varied in nature, each of these is capable of adding to or detracting from our physical enjoyment of life.

One such function is to receive sensory stimuli and to transmit them to the brain as nerve impulses. These stimuli are set off by pressure, changes in temperature and tissue damage, and produce sensations of touch, warmth, cold and pain, as well as an awareness of comfort or discomfort. Some anthropologists and psychiatrists, indeed, regard the skin as an important factor in the foundation of a happy family relationship. They hold that when an infant is bathed and cuddled, the skin becomes the means by which he first receives affection and a sense of security from his mother.

The skin transmits sensory impulses more readily from some areas than others, depending upon the abundance of nerve fibers in a particular area. On the face, the soles of the feet and the palms of the hands, these fibers are densely packed within the skin. This explains, for example, why facial pain is often more accurately localized than pain elsewhere in the body. It also explains why blind people can read Braille through their fingertips.

SUNTAN AND FRECKLES
Every person's skin (except in the case of albinos) produces a certain amount of melanin, a dark pigment which absorbs ultraviolet light. Cells called melanocytes produce this pigment at rates which speed up on exposure to sunlight. When they speed up, the skin darkens—hence the sunbather's tan. If the sunbather's enthusiasm outstrips the rate at which his melanocytes can produce pigment, excess ultraviolet light—by means not fully understood—causes the release of a chemical in the skin that makes the blood vessels swell and the skin become red and sore. Groups of active melanocytes surrounded by groups of less active melanocytes produce the islands of pigment known as freckles.

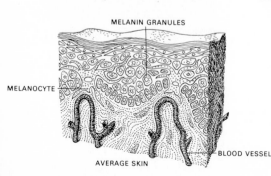

MELANIN GRANULES

MELANOCYTE

AVERAGE SKIN

BLOOD VESSEL

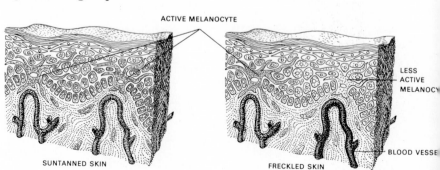

ACTIVE MELANOCYTE

LESS ACTIVE MELANOCY

SUNTANNED SKIN

FRECKLED SKIN

BLOOD VESSE

Another essential function of the skin is to help put a brake on any tendency of the body to grow too hot or too cold. The main regulator of bodily temperature is located in a part of the brain known as the hypothalamus. Its collaboration with the skin is close and continuing. The hypothalamus has two thermostats, one to register a rise and one to register a drop in normal body temperatures. At a signal from one thermostat, indicating overheating of the body, circulation of the blood to the skin is stepped up, and the heat from the internal organs is carried into a network of small blood vessels just underneath the skin, there to be dissipated. Simultaneously the same thermostat spurs the activity of the sweat glands. Millions of these glands lie coiled deep in the dermis and in the subcutaneous tissue; they open onto the skin surface through the pores. The increased perspiration which results is evaporated when it comes into contact with moving air outside the body; this provides efficient cooling-off.

Conversely, when the other thermostat in the hypothalamus signals a drop in body temperature, the flow of blood to the skin slows down and the sweat glands produce less. As the outward rush of blood dwindles, the skin itself and the layer of fat beneath it function as insulators to conserve whatever bodily heat there is. One physiologist has estimated that a body swathed in clothes is only a quarter more efficiently insulated than a body that is stark-naked. The natural insulation is even better in the case of the female body, with its more abundant deposits of fat—an estimated 28 per cent of the body's mass as opposed to a mere 18 per cent for the male.

The virtues of fat

Despite its virtue as a guardian of bodily heat, fat is seldom appreciated; its possessor is more often busy maligning it. Yet fatty tissue serves more than one useful and admirable purpose. It furnishes an emergency food supply in the event that normal sustenance is stopped. It provides a shock absorber that prevents injury to bone except at relatively exposed areas such as the skull, the collarbone or the shin. It helps form the body's pleasantly rounded contours. Where fat should cease to be welcome is the point at which it becomes excess. Fashion trends and the tastes of the time can help dictate when fat becomes extreme; today, for instance, the slender body is greatly prized in much of the world, while 300 years ago, a plumper silhouette was the fashion follower's ideal. The physiological costs of obesity can help determine when fat has become excessive—by contributing to heart disease or diabetes, for instance, or by increasing the risk to both mother and child during pregnancy, or by causing men to become sterile.

The question of what constitutes excess, short of obesity, has no pat answer. A great deal depends, however, on the size of the skeletal structure to which the fat is attached, and the variations that are possible in this structure are countless. One homespun measure that is sometimes applied is to grasp, between the thumb and forefinger, the skin at the side of the body just above the waistline. If the thickness amounts to more than an inch, the fat is presumed to be excessive. But this particular rule of thumb is far from being infallible. Many doctors, when confronted by a patient who poses the problem of the degree of surplus, present him with a statistical table of average weights to ponder and leave the rest to his conscience and his mirror.

Fat and other controllable features of the human body are united with features determined by heredity and by the glands to create the illimitable combinations which stamp each man as unique. The range of features is so immense that no two individuals are exactly alike. The body simply defies convenient pigeonholing.

At best, attempts to place people in categories produce broad generalizations, and even to these broad divisions the exceptions are legion. Efforts along this line have been undertaken in almost every century since the beginning of civilization. Some were born simply of a passion for orderliness. Some were made with a view to determining possible relationships between physique and various illnesses and diseases, and indeed between the outer and inner self. The great Aristotle, for example, was convinced that a man's character could be read merely by noting the shape of his nose.

One system for sorting people into distinguishable types was to classify them according to race. Among the first to attempt this approach was Johann Friedrich Blumenbach, a young 18th Century German zoologist. Blumenbach used only one physical criterion: skin color. In time, successive classifiers set forth other external characteristics—the shape of the face, the texture of the hair and so on—that might make individuals identifiable not only by race, but by subrace as well.

A new view of human diversity

By the end of the 19th Century, anthropologists who traveled to far-flung—and heretofore inaccessible—lands began to observe that clearcut differences between the world's populations simply did not exist. These scientists noticed that the people of India, for example, exhibited both the long nose of Caucasoids and the dark skin of Negroids. Perhaps even more revealing was the discovery that neighboring populations tended to share similar physical traits while distant populations tended to be physically distinguishable from one another.

Out of all these observations emerged a new view of human diversity. No longer was each individual seen to possess traits typical of a particular

INFANT ABOUT SIX MONTHS OLD

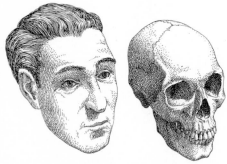

ADULT ABOUT 30 YEARS OLD

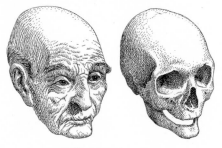

ADULT ABOUT 80 YEARS OLD

THE AGING OF A FACE
Aging is most apparent in the face, not only because of its effects on skin but because of skull changes as well. The drawings above illustrate the process. The infant's jaws are small compared to his braincase, still with the so-called "soft spot" on top; his chipmunklike jowls are layers of fat called sucking cushions. As he matures, his jaws lengthen and his braincase becomes dome-shaped. By advanced age, degeneration of bone has shrunk the skull, and wear on the teeth—or loss of teeth—shortens the distance from nose to chin. Skin and muscles atrophy and the face sags in wrinkles upon the diminished skull.

race, but rather to embody variations of the same human traits. Because the proteins that enable the body to grow and display these traits are controlled by hereditary units, called genes, a precise method of measuring differences between individuals has been to analyze their proteins, a technique known as electrophoresis. First used in 1949 by the American chemist Linus Pauling and his associates at the California Institute of Technology, it involved applying an electric field to a solution of proteins. Those proteins with different electrical charges moved about the field at different rates and eventually separated.

With the use of this technique, researchers concluded that genes among people of the same geographic population were not in fact the same. And more than that, the resulting 200,000 or so differences in proteins between two individuals who were classified as Chinese turned out to be only slightly fewer than the differences that appeared when one of them was compared with a European, or with an African. In other words, the differences *between* populations were found to be only slightly greater than the differences *within* populations.

At the heart of these differences is a process called mutation, wherein a change occurs, purely by chance, in the composition of an inherited gene. When this accidental alteration is repeated over many generations, great numbers of people are affected by it. Almost always, the effect is negative, as with those carrying the gene responsible for hemophilia, the failure of the blood to clot. In rare, but important, instances, genetic mutations can result in distinct benefits. A gene altered for the better stands a good chance of being passed on to future generations, and may eventually replace the original gene.

Scientists generally believe that this genetic "survival of the fittest" stems from the body's tendency to adapt to its environment. A case in point is the human nose. As with other physical traits, the variations here—from long, narrow noses to short, broad ones—suggest a strong correlation with climate rather than with geographical proximity. Long noses tend to prevail in bone-dry regions like the Middle East, in contrast to the short, broad noses that are characteristic of people who live in moist, tropical climates.

A look at humanity's future

How human beings will look 10,000 years, half a million years or even a million years from now is anybody's guess. Some anthropologists predict a physique that will be dramatically different from anything we know today; others paint an unpalatable picture of a creature who is much like ourselves but who has little or no hair and few, if any, teeth. And still others argue that the human exterior actually will stay pretty much the same as it is in the 20th Century.

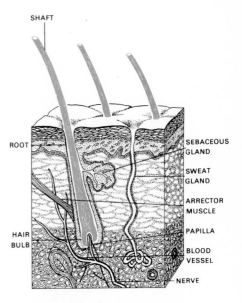

THE HUMAN HAIR
Virtually the entire human skin is covered with hair, though much of it is too fine to be visible. It is relatively vestigial compared to the hair covering of other primates, but it still serves a purpose, if only by being highly sensitive to touch. The part above the skin is the shaft; below the surface is the root. The root, bulbous at the bottom, is enclosed in a follicle surrounded by fine nerves. Connective tissue at the base of the bulb (the papilla) contains other nerve fibers, capillaries and occasional pigment cells. Sebaceous glands secrete lubricating oil, and the arrector muscles can literally make hair stand on end.

On one point, though, there is agreement. Humanity in the future must continue to adapt—biologically, culturally and technologically—to conditions affecting its survival. Along these lines, scientists offer some reasonable expectations for the future:

• Intelligence per se will probably not increase, and may even decline slightly. Evidence is seen in the fact that the size of the brain, bearing as it does a rough correlation with learning ability, has not changed in more than 150,000 years. Apparently, when early man reached a point at which he could create a culture, the need to increase intelligence dropped and so did the need for a larger cranial capacity.

• In places like the United States and western Europe, where the birth rate has been steadily declining, older people will soon outnumber the young. An indication of this trend is the increasing median age; in less than 200 years, it has practically doubled—thanks to more abundant and more varied food, better sanitation and advances in medicine. Over a period of time, a similar trend can be expected to occur in less developed societies throughout the world.

Obviously, no one can predict with any certainty how mankind will react to the challenges posed by these developments. Still, the human track record over several million years gives cause for optimism that resourcefulness will not be lacking.

An Atlas of the Anatomy

In the 400 years that have passed since Vesalius launched a revolution in medical science with the accuracy and detail of his anatomical opus, *De Humani Corporis Fabrica*, the firsthand study of the dissected body has become the foundation of man's knowledge of the human organism. Anatomy offers both an over-all look at the body's structure and a first glimpse of how it functions. To the uninitiated, the anatomy appears to be a conglomeration of bone and muscle, oddly shaped internal organs, and networks of blood vessels and nerves. But generations of anatomists have organized the many parts of the body into separate anatomical systems and named their parts. Echoing Vesalius' book, which set figures against miniature landscapes, the pictures on these pages show these systems—skeletal, muscular, circulatory, nervous and visceral—in the form of shadowy athletes against fanciful backgrounds; the parts bear their scientific names.

A HOUSE FOR THE BRAIN

A ghostly ensemble of 22 bones and toothy grin, the human skull *(opposite)* consists of a rigid cranium in which the delicate brain is safely stored, and the facial skeleton with its movable lower jaw, which enables man to talk and eat. The tiny holes, or foramina, on the forehead, cheekbone and jaw are the orifices through which nerves pass to and from the brain and the skin.

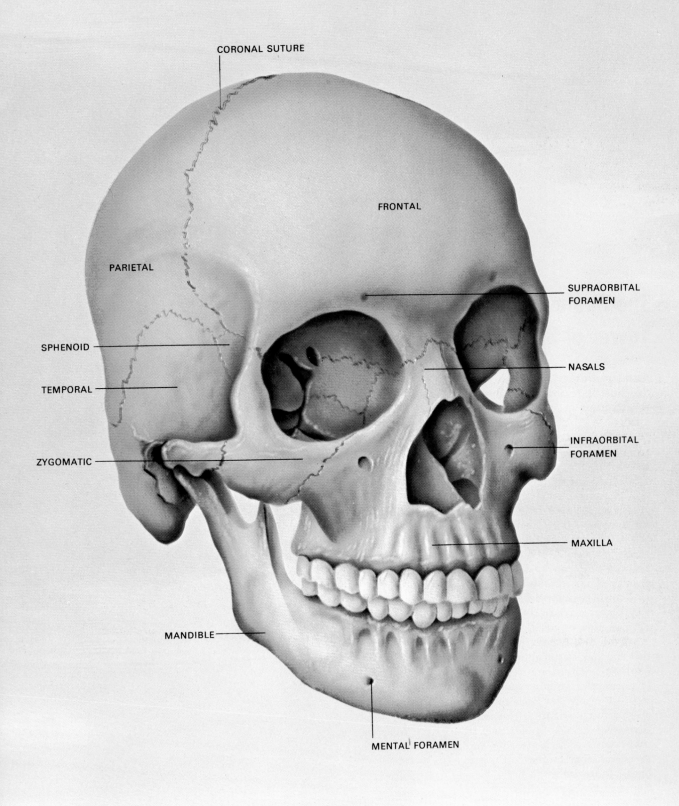

CORONAL SUTURE

FRONTAL

PARIETAL

SUPRAORBITAL
FORAMEN

SPHENOID

NASALS

TEMPORAL

INFRAORBITAL
FORAMEN

ZYGOMATIC

MAXILLA

MANDIBLE

MENTAL FORAMEN

The Skeleton: Tower of Strength

Man's skeleton was shaped by his decision more than a million years ago to stand erect. The skeleton is a tower of bones put together with hinges and joints—a leverage system so superbly rigged and balanced that he can run, jump and bend despite his small feet. The adult's 206 bones anchor his muscles and shield his vital organs with a great variety of structural shapes—from the flat plates of the skull to the backbone's hollow rings. Strong yet pliant, they have adapted with varying degrees of success to man's unique posture. The skeleton of no other creature has such long legs relative to the arms, a foot with so high an arch, and such remarkable hands—freed for use as tool-making instruments with opposing thumbs once they were no longer needed for running on or grasping tree branches. His backbone is less perfectly adapted. Humans are born with straight spines, but after they learn to walk they acquire another unique characteristic—the sway-back—the price of an erect stance.

BONY SHOCK ABSORBERS
Although bones can break, they are so strong that man can engage in unnatural feats like pole-vaulting without shattering into shards. The tubular thigh bones of the pole vaulter at right may take up to 20,000 pounds of pressure per square inch (137,900 kPa) when he lands.

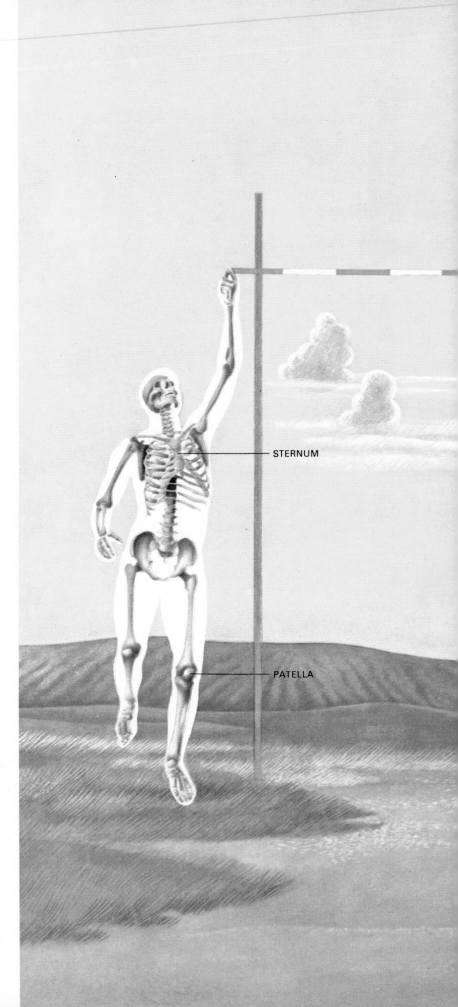

STERNUM

PATELLA

44

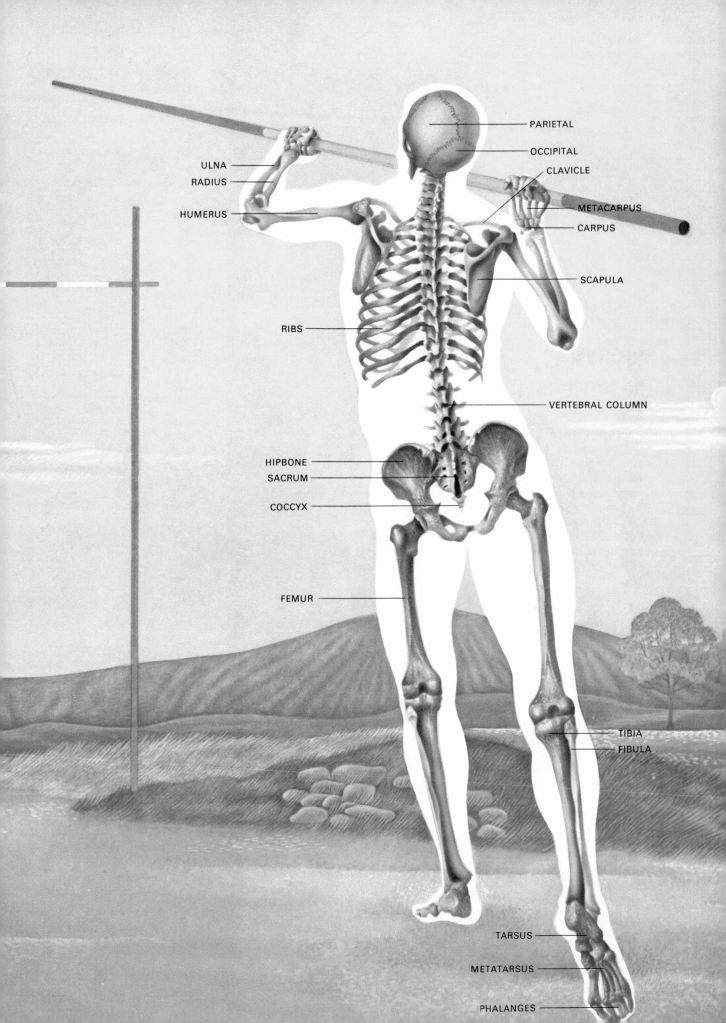

PARIETAL

OCCIPITAL

CLAVICLE

ULNA

RADIUS

METACARPUS

HUMERUS

CARPUS

SCAPULA

RIBS

VERTEBRAL COLUMN

HIPBONE

SACRUM

COCCYX

FEMUR

TIBIA

FIBULA

TARSUS

METATARSUS

PHALANGES

Muscles:
The Power of Pull

The body's 600-odd muscles are the cables whose pull on bones makes motion possible. Their sole function is contraction. By working in pairs, however—one muscle contracting to pull a bone forward, the other to pull it back—the muscular system is capable of an immense variety of movements, from tripping the tongue in speech to running a race.

The action of muscle on bone is most apparent in the bending of arms and legs, whose solid shafts of bone are pulled into motion by the contraction of muscles surrounding them. Other, less movable, bones are also tugged; for example, muscles of the upper torso move the bones of the rib cage during breathing by contracting and relaxing. Muscles also pull on skin or other muscles, as in a smile, a frown, and the rise and fall of the diaphragm. All these contractions are controlled and coordinated by the brain. So interrelated are muscles that one contraction usually involves many others. The racer, exercising many muscles, even grins as he runs.

MUSCLES ON THE RUN
The racers on the beach at right run by rhythmically contracting alternate teams of muscles. Muscles pictured in red are called flexors; their contractions bend hinge joints such as the knees. Muscles shown in gray are called extensors; their contractions straighten the knees again.

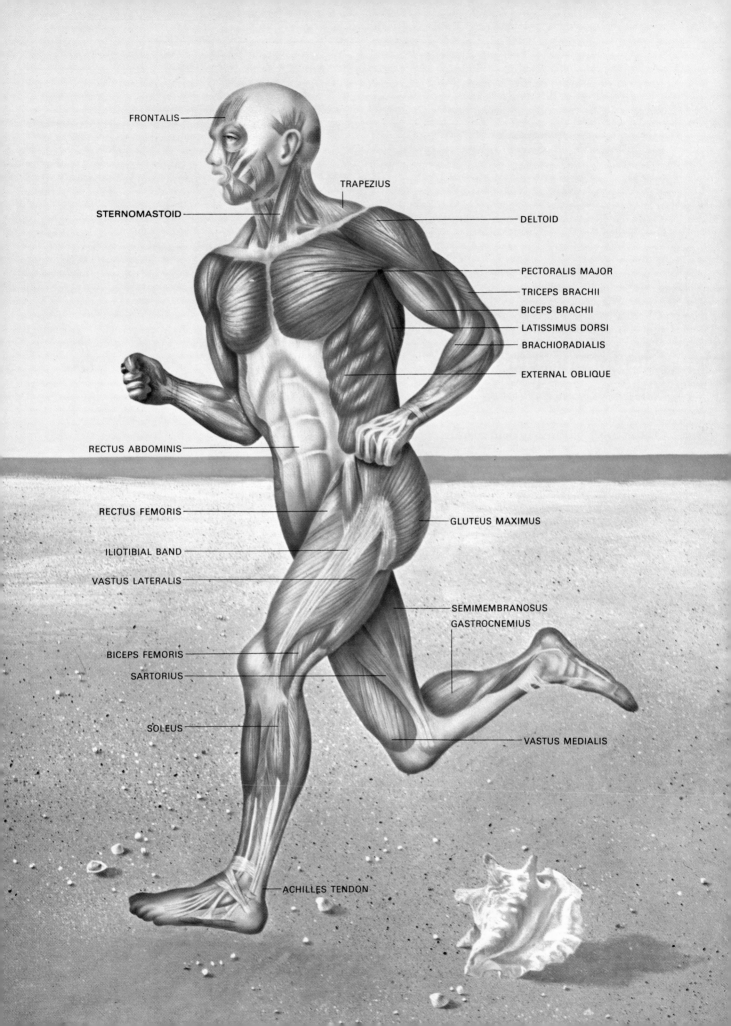

FRONTALIS

TRAPEZIUS

STERNOMASTOID

DELTOID

PECTORALIS MAJOR

TRICEPS BRACHII

BICEPS BRACHII

LATISSIMUS DORSI

BRACHIORADIALIS

EXTERNAL OBLIQUE

RECTUS ABDOMINIS

RECTUS FEMORIS

GLUTEUS MAXIMUS

ILIOTIBIAL BAND

VASTUS LATERALIS

SEMIMEMBRANOSUS

GASTROCNEMIUS

BICEPS FEMORIS

SARTORIUS

SOLEUS

VASTUS MEDIALIS

ACHILLES TENDON

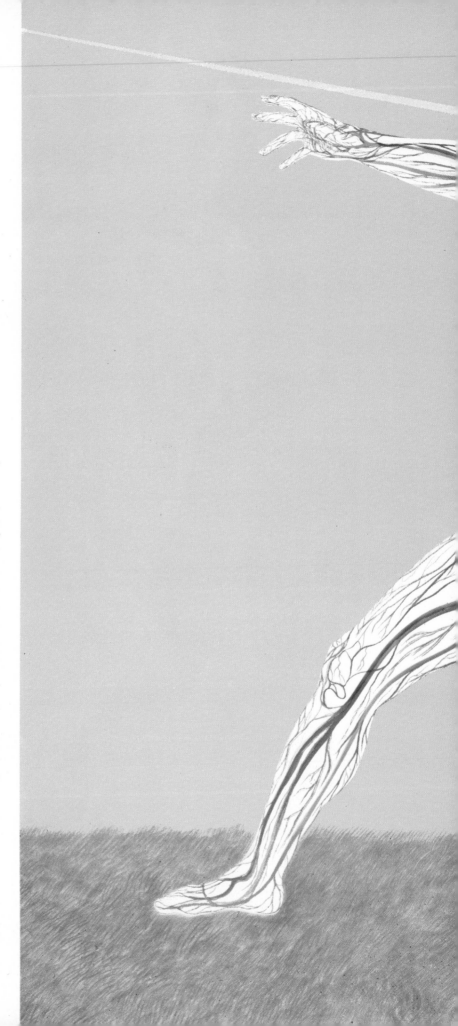

The Circulation: One-way Network

The network pictured at right comprises some 60,000 miles (97,000 km) of tubing which carries blood to every part of the body. Its most impressive feature is its circular manner of keeping the blood moving, always away from the heart in the arteries, toward the heart in the veins—in spite of gravity and in spite of millions of alternate routes. The pump of the heart gives the flow its force, sending freshly oxygenated blood surging out the aorta, the body's largest artery, and into subsidiary arteries, even to the top of the head. The arteries branch out into smaller arterioles, which in turn branch out into millions of microscopic capillaries. These capillaries eventually unite to form venules, which unite into veins, thin-walled vessels with interior valves which prevent the blood from slipping backward. Thus the spent blood streams back to the heart. A side trip to the lungs via a pulmonary network refreshes it with oxygen, and it returns to the heart ready to start anew. The entire cycle takes less than a minute.

SUPPLY ON DEMAND
The arteries *(red)* and veins *(blue)* of muscles doing energy-consuming work, such as javelin-throwing, may receive up to nine times more blood than when at rest. Muscles in arterial walls, on signals from the nervous system, can contract so that the flow goes where needed.

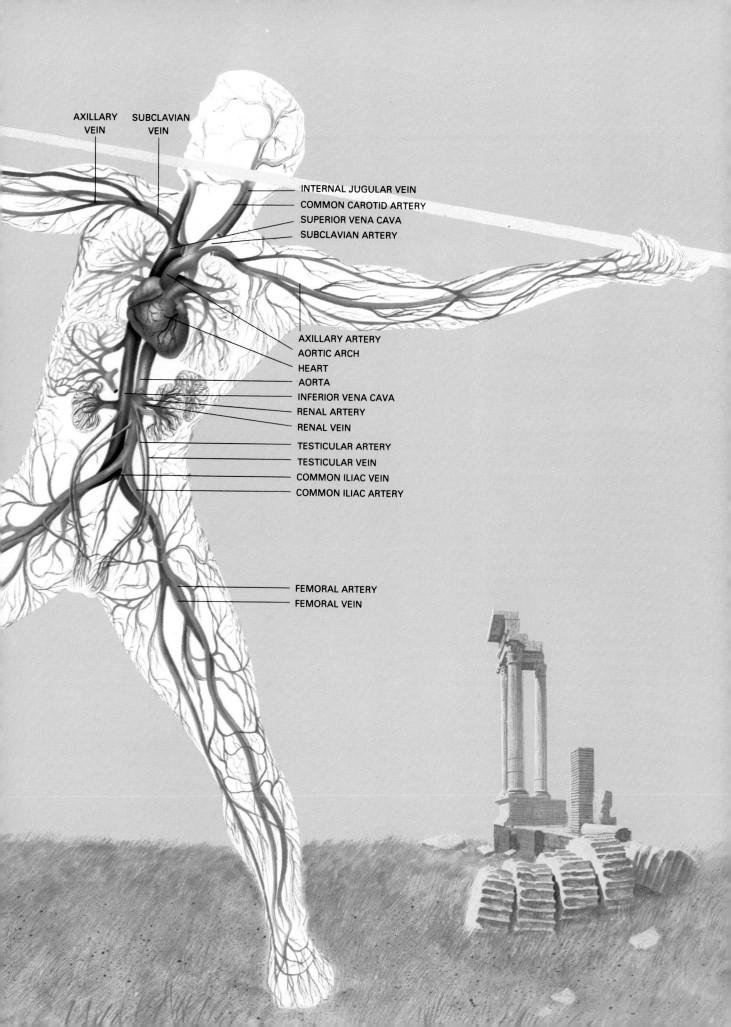

AXILLARY
VEIN

SUBCLAVIAN
VEIN

INTERNAL JUGULAR VEIN
COMMON CAROTID ARTERY
SUPERIOR VENA CAVA
SUBCLAVIAN ARTERY

AXILLARY ARTERY
AORTIC ARCH
HEART
AORTA
INFERIOR VENA CAVA
RENAL ARTERY
RENAL VEIN
TESTICULAR ARTERY
TESTICULAR VEIN
COMMON ILIAC VEIN
COMMON ILIAC ARTERY

FEMORAL ARTERY
FEMORAL VEIN

Nervous System:
Sorter of Signals

The intricate task of receiving and reacting to the storm of stimuli that assault the human body is charged to the nervous system. Made up of the brain, the spinal cord and a complex network of nerves, the nervous system coordinates all the body's activities, in response to signals from both inside and outside the body. The brain is the system's headquarters. From it stem cranial nerves and the spinal cord, a cylinder of nerve tissue that runs through the backbone for 18 inches (46 cm). Nerves branch out from it on either side, to embrace the body from head to toe. Some are sensory nerves, which carry stimuli to the spinal cord and brain. Others are motor nerves, along which the brain sends its orders. We react to some stimuli consciously, as we do when we swat a fly. Other activities—such as those of the viscera—are generally outside conscious control. But we can teach ourselves to be aware of these otherwise involuntary activities—such as muscle tension or high blood pressure—and to control them.

THE PATH OF NEURAL MESSAGES
The nerve impulse that trips this athlete moves at a speed of nearly 350 feet (107 m) per second—much faster than the discus he throws. From the brain the signal flashes through the spinal cord to a motor nerve. From there, with a chemical boost, it triggers a muscle.

50

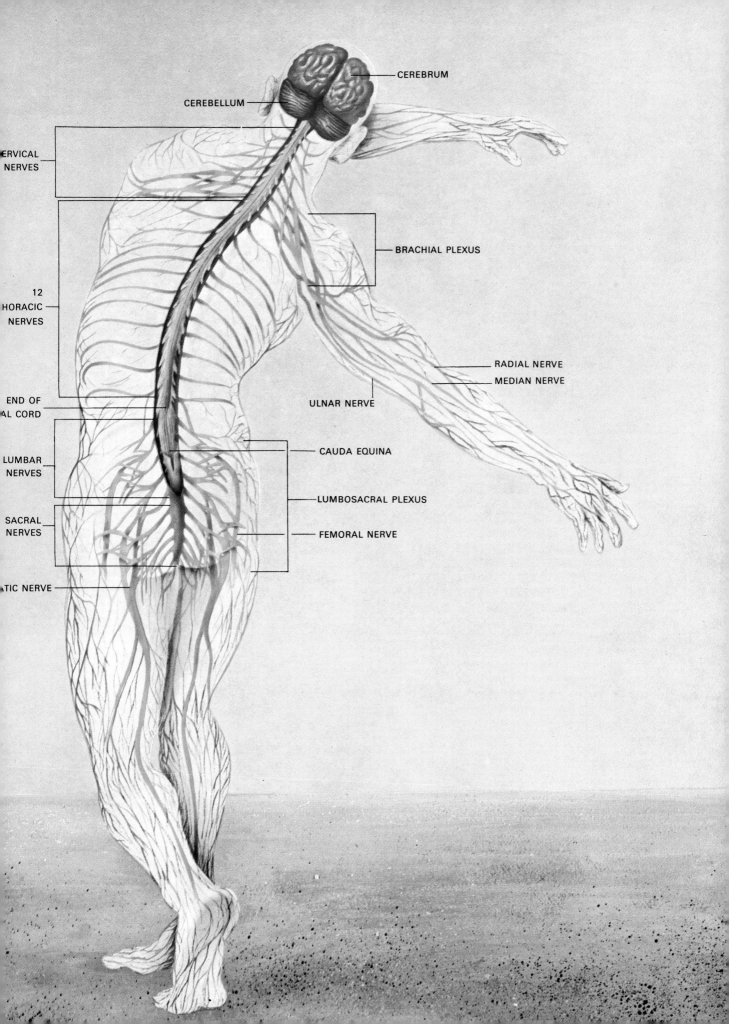

CEREBRUM

CEREBELLUM

ERVICAL
NERVES

BRACHIAL PLEXUS

12
HORACIC
NERVES

RADIAL NERVE

MEDIAN NERVE

ULNAR NERVE

END OF
AL CORD

CAUDA EQUINA

LUMBAR
NERVES

LUMBOSACRAL PLEXUS

SACRAL
NERVES

FEMORAL NERVE

TIC NERVE

The Viscera:
Fueling the Body

Although they are often called by a single name, the viscera, the neatly packed organs that fill the body's chest and abdominal cavities belong to several different systems—respiratory, digestive and urinary—which together provide the body with food and oxygen and remove wastes.

The trachea and lungs are parts of the respiratory system, which delivers oxygen to the blood. The lungs consist of millions of elastic membranous sacs which together can hold about as much air as a basketball.

The organs of the digestive system —most prominently the stomach, the large and small intestines and the liver—modify foods which the body takes in. The soft, reddish-brown liver, the largest gland in the body, literally plays hundreds of roles, from producing proteins to secreting bile.

The bladder is part of the urinary system, which regulates the body's water supply. The kidneys, located behind the stomach and liver, filter out wastes and pass them along to the bladder for storage and disposal.

VERSATILE SACS AND TUBES
If a living chest and abdominal flap were peeled back, the viscera would only approximate those pictured here. The lungs, for example, are constantly inflating and emptying; the 10-inch-long (25.4-cm) stomach can shrink to a flattened sac or expand to hold two quarts (1.9 l) of food.

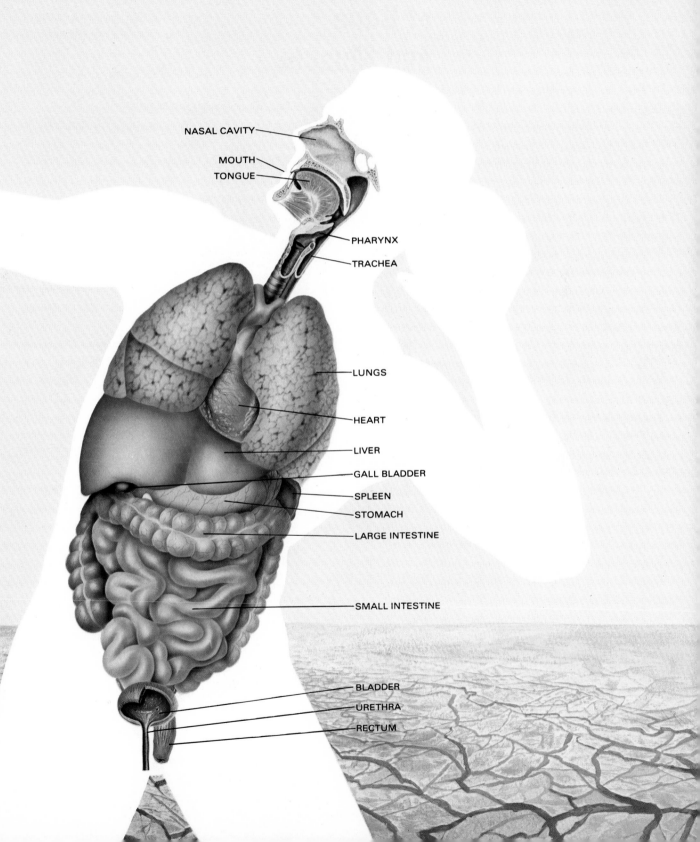

NASAL CAVITY

MOUTH

TONGUE

PHARYNX

TRACHEA

LUNGS

HEART

LIVER

GALL BLADDER

SPLEEN

STOMACH

LARGE INTESTINE

SMALL INTESTINE

BLADDER

URETHRA

RECTUM

3

The Team
of Bone
and Muscle

A CASE OF COORDINATION
In order to accomplish this deceptively simple-looking straddle jump, U.S. Olympics gymnast star Abie Grossfeld springs high into the air in a superb display of the workings of the body's musculoskeletal system. Even in nonathletes the daily pounding to which bones and muscles are subjected is so great that it would cause some machines to wear out after only a few years.

ONE NEW YEAR'S EVE a few years ago a small sports car skidded on an icy curve in Snoqualmie Pass in the Cascades and plunged through a guardrail down a rocky slope into the creek bed below. The driver died instantly. His 23-year-old companion was still breathing when rescuers arrived, but she looked—as one of them put it—as if every bone in her body were broken.

X-rays bore out that amateur diagnosis to an alarming extent. They showed eight ribs smashed on one side of the chest, three on the other. The left shoulder was dislocated. Several separate fracture lines criss-crossed the pelvis. The left thigh bone had snapped in the middle. No X-rays were needed to reveal the damage to the left leg; both its bones protruded in a dirty open break. "She may live," the hospital surgeon said, "but only in a wheelchair."

A little more than two years later his patient was off crutches and set to embark upon a normal life of marriage and childbearing. Skilled surgical techniques and drugs had vitally contributed to her comeback. But two other forces also played a powerful part: the extraordinary capacity of bone to mend itself, and the natural tendency of torn muscle to heal back into usefulness.

With its built-in ability for self-repair, the human framework represents a triumph of design and engineering that puts any bridge or skyscraper to shame. It has its flaws, to be sure. An S-shaped spine, for example, burdens us with aching backs and other ills—a result of man's decision to stop moving about on all fours and rear up on his hindquarters. But offsetting any structural imperfection is a funtional skill responsive both to crisis and to the demands of everyday life.

The three basic elements of the musculoskeletal system—bone, muscle and connective tissue—normally perform with perfect teamwork. Their mission is to support the body, shield its delicate internal organs and make it mobile. No task force was ever more meticulously equipped and organized:
• Support for the body is supplied by the bones. Individually strong as iron girders, they are, in addition, linked by ligaments—bands of elastic, fibrous tissue—and fitted together, end to end, in joints.
• Protection for the internal organs is provided, in concert, by the bones, joints and connective tissue. Where bone movement would be dangerous, as in the pelvis or skull, the joints are rigid—glued together or even interlocked. Where movement is essential, as in the hips or shoulders, the joints are flexible—lined with cartilage, a glassy-smooth tissue which reduces friction, and lubricated by synovial fluid, a secretion of watery consistency which acts as a "joint oil."
• Mobility for the body is supplied by the skeletal muscles. These are separate and distinct from the muscles of the internal organs, such as

the visceral muscles of the stomach and intestine, and from the special cardiac muscles of the heart. The internal muscles have no relation to the bony skeleton, and they operate, in general, without conscious control —although experiments indicate that conscious control may be learned. Biofeedback training—teaching people to recognize and control movements and bodily processes previously thought to be wholly involuntary— is being used by some doctors as an aid in treating cardiac and hypertensive patients. And accident and stroke victims, through biofeedback training, can regain some control over nonfunctioning skeletal muscles. In contrast to the internal muscles, the skeletal muscles are voluntary and, unless injured in some way, are subject to command. Most are attached to bone by bands of tissue called tendons. Usually these muscles are paired. While one muscle "stands," relaxed, its partner tugs at the bone, much like ropes pulling at a lever.

A kick and a teeter

Supported by bone and activated by muscle, the body enjoys an incredibly wide range of movement, as forceful as sledge-hammering, as gentle as blinking. The same hand that pats a puppy pounds a desk. The same foot that teeters on tiptoe kicks a field goal. The limits of mobility are broad and the limitations relatively few; we cannot, for example, touch left forefinger to left elbow, or turn the head to look directly behind us. Even so, by stretching ligaments and muscles in order to make his joints unusually limber, a yoga practitioner can tie himself into a mariner's knot, wrap his feet around his neck, twist his spine and otherwise contort himself.

The grand plan of the musculoskeletal structure is all the more impressive because of the sheer number of its parts. A mature body contains more than 600 muscles and 206 bones, not counting the tiny sesamoid bones—like sesame seeds—embedded in the tendons of the thumb, big toe and other pressure points. For the bones, in fact, the figure represents a comedown; newborn babes may have more than 300. By adulthood many of these bones have fused. Not infrequently, however, fusion fails. An otherwise average person may find himself with an extra bone in the arch of the foot, and one in every 20 people has an extra rib. This appendage appears three times as often in men as in women—possibly a form of compensation for the rib Adam yielded up to Eve.

Except for these minor anomalies, the arrangement of the bones is as precise, orderly and purposeful as the parent skeletal system itself, and their distribution from top to bottom is a strikingly equable one. The skull, at the apex of the bony structure, has 29 bones. The spine, to which are attached the shoulder girdle, rib cage and hip girdle, has 26 vertebrae. The ribs number 24. The two girdles, so named because of

GETTING THE INSIDE PICTURE
How the X-ray machine, that valuable diagnostic tool, works is diagramed below. A current heats a cathode, which ejects a stream of electrons. The electrons hit a target on the face of the anode, producing X-rays, which are reflected and pass through the patient. A collimator regulates the size of the area being X-rayed, and a lead shield protects the patient's reproductive system from radiation. Some tissues, such as bone, block more rays than other tissues, and appear on special X-ray film *(in the cassette)* as lighter areas of gray, producing a black-and-white picture of the inner man.

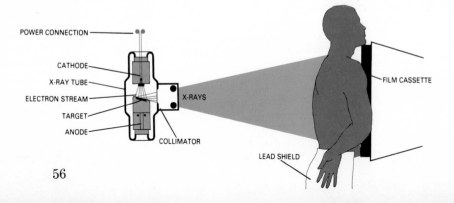

POWER CONNECTION
CATHODE
X-RAY TUBE
ELECTRON STREAM
X-RAYS
TARGET
ANODE
COLLIMATOR
FILM CASSETTE
LEAD SHIELD

56

their formation, mark the upper and lower limits of the body's trunk, or central area. From them, respectively, stem the bones of the upper and lower limbs—each with 30 bones apiece. Of the 60 bones in the two upper limbs, all but six are concentrated in the hands and wrists; of the 60 bones in the two lower limbs, all but eight are concentrated in the ankles and feet. Thus, appropriately, more than half of all the bones in the body support those parts of it which maintain the busiest daily work schedule—our extremities.

Bones are generally classified into four types according to shape: long, short, flat or irregular. They range in size from the all-powerful thigh bone, or femur—about 20 inches (51 cm) long, more than an inch across at mid-shaft—to the pisiform, the smallest of the wrist bones, shaped like a split pea; this bone lies at the base of the little finger, familiarly known as the pinkie. But whatever their size or shape, almost every bone in the body fits a particular need. The most notable exception is the coccyx, man's vestigial tail.

The femur, for example, must withstand great weight and pressure. Its shaft is shaped like a hollow cylinder—an excellent design, as any engineer knows, for maximum strength with a minimum of material. Thus constructed, the thigh bone can take enormous pressures, depending upon the weight of the person and the activity at the moment. In a 125-pound (57-kg) woman who is simply taking a walk, for example, some points of the femur withstand a pressure of 1,200 pounds per square inch (8,274 kPa). If by some whim, she were suddenly to start jumping, this bone would be equally capable of resisting the far greater stresses involved.

Another superb example of functionalism appears in a typical vertebra of the spinal column. To help bear the weight of the body, it is formed like a solid cylinder. At the back of the cylinder, a bony ring permits passage of the spinal nerve cord, and also serves to protect it. At the back of the ring are three sharp projections, or spurs, which join with the ribs and anchor the muscles of the back.

Safe conduct in the skull

The bones which guard the various vital internal organs are also especially adapted to their assignments. The skull, the pelvis and the rib cage all provide noteworthy examples. In the skull, the bones which encase the brain are—in contrast to the wafer-thin bones of the face—thick plates, interlocked at the edges. They actually fuse when the brain reaches its mature growth. In both the male and female pelvis, the bones, while not interlocked, are tightly bound by cartilaginous joints; but in the female, during the last stage of pregnancy, these joints loosen and separate slightly to make childbirth easier. In the rib cage, which is designed to defend the heart, lungs, liver and spleen against damage,

PUTTING THE PIECES BACK TOGETHER AGAIN

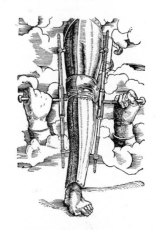

THE EARLY BONESETTERS
A growing efficiency in weapons created a demand for bonesetting devices, such as the 16th Century German leg splint *(above)* and arm stretcher *(below)*. The Greeks knew about splints, starched bandages and clay casts, and in the Fifth Century B.C. Hippocrates was treating fractures with sound techniques. In the 14th Century weights and pulleys came into use as traction devices for keeping broken limbs properly aligned.

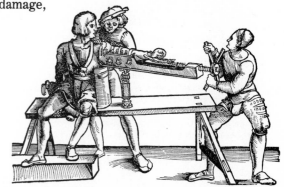

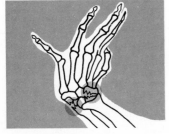

A FOOTBALL FRACTURE
Different sports impose different strains on the human frame and cause different kinds of bone breaks. The fractures shown here are common. The break above occurs when the defensive player's wrist is bent backward by the ballcarrier's momentum. His wrist will be immobilized for six to eight weeks; it should heal in eight to 12 weeks.

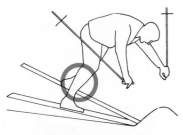

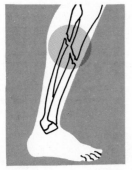

A BROKEN LEG FOR A SKIER
This skier has just plowed into a sitzmark (literally, a "sit-mark") left by another skier. His feet are stopped in their tracks; the rest of his body continues its downhill plunge, and the resulting strain breaks the two bones of his lower leg. The fracture will normally take from four to six months before it is completely healed.

the ribs curve out from the upper vertebrae, in barrel-stave fashion, to provide a packing-crate type of protection.

The rib cage, or thorax, also provides an excellent example of another marvel of the skeletal structure: the versatility of the joints. While rigidly protecting its precious cargo, the thorax must be able to expand and contract to permit the lungs to inflate and deflate with each breath. In front, the ribs are joined firmly to the breastbone by cartilage, but in back they are furnished with tiny gliding, rotating joints which enable them to articulate individually with the vertebrae. In contrast to these minuscule joints is the great ball-and-socket joint of the hip, which holds the rounded ball end of the femur in a fistlike grasp. Perhaps the finest proof of this joint's range of flexibility is the right-angle stance of the ballerina or of the baseball pitcher at windup.

Other joints, however, may limit motion to very specific planes (in some people the limits extend a bit more than usual, an attribute inaccurately described as double-jointedness). The knee can move only as a simple hinge. The shoulder, which can easily be dislocated if the arm rotates too widely, has a far shallower ball-and-socket joint than the hip. The head enjoys a smooth rotary motion, thanks to the two uppermost vertebrae in the neck, the atlas, named for the Greek god who carried the world on his shoulders, and the axis, which serves as a pivot for both head and atlas. It is the collaborative movements of these bones that produces two of mankind's most overworked gestures—a negative shake of the head and an affirmative nod.

However diverse in action, all bone is amazingly strong and at the same time amazingly light. In a 160-pound (72.6-kg) man only about 29 pounds (13 kg) represent bone weight. Steel bars of comparable size would weigh at least four or five times as much. The lightness of bone is due in part to its porosity, in part to the hollow-tube construction of the long bones of the limbs. The strength is due to bone's composition. About half its weight is made up of inorganic compounds of calcium, phosphorus and other minerals; about a quarter is made up of organic matter—a type of protein fiber called collagen, from the Greek *kolla*, glue, and *gène*, forming; almost all the remaining quarter of bone weight is, surprisingly, water. The minerals and collagen are cemented together—like steel rods and concrete in making reinforced concrete—to produce great rigidity.

A bone to pick with Shakespeare

Bone's mineral content also accounts for its most notable characteristic—its hardness. The shafts of long bones are virtually as hard as granite; even in the spongy, rounded bone ends, which are relatively softer, the shape is retained long after the body itself is dead. Bone is thus the body's most enduring monument. Shakespeare was only partly right when he made his celebrated observation that the good men do is oft interred with their bones; a lot more is buried with it.

So durable is bone, in fact, that it provides our major clues to humanity's past. Skeletal remains many centuries old have helped scientists deduce the size and shape of ancient peoples, the kind of work they did, and the arthritis and other ailments they suffered. Recently, anthropologists have uncovered evidence suggesting that beings with human features existed much further back than a million years ago, which was once believed to be the outer limit. In 1974 nearly one half of a skeleton was discovered by Dr. Donald Johanson in the fossil beds at Hadar, in the remote Afar Desert of Ethiopia. The remains were of a female creature, believed to date back about three million years, who stood about three and a half feet tall, walked erect, had a skeletal structure and joints similar to man's from the neck down, and yet possessed the small brain and large canine teeth of an ape. This hominid skeleton (dubbed "Lucy" by Johanson and formally christened *Australopithecus afarensis)*, other fossil fragments discovered by Dr. Johanson, and fossilized footprints and bones found by Dr. Mary Leakey, working separately in Tanzania, provide strong evidence that man's ancestors were walking erect at least three million years ago.

Skeletons and time clocks

The sex, approximate age, race and medical history of a person long deceased are among other data preserved by bone. The telltale marks are many. Dr. Wilton M. Krogman, professor of physical anthropology at the University of Pennsylvania, and long renowned among police and insurance men for his skill as a bone detective, has, for example, determined the sex of a murder victim by the size of ridges above the eyes and at the back of the skull. He has been able to judge age, give or take a few years, by ascertaining whether the long bones and wisdom teeth were fully grown and whether the seams of the skull bones were fully fused; at the age of 40, for example, they are about three quarters fused. Another technique he has employed as a clue to age is to X-ray decalcified areas in the shoulder blades. Here, as elsewhere in the body, the loss of calcium irreversibly increases with the years. "From birth to death," Dr. Krogman notes, "the skeleton punches a time clock."

Throughout this inexorable process, however, bone continues its basic job of supporting the body and providing the joint articulations needed for smooth, effortless movement. It performs so inconspicuously that only some malfunction reminds us of its presence. The joints may become inflamed and swollen, resulting in the painful, crippling condition we know as arthritis. Simple wear and tear on the cartilage of the weight-bearing joints in particular may cause the form of arthritis we call "old folks' rheumatism." A part of one of the "disks" of the spinal column—thick

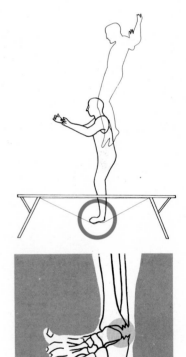

A TOUGH BREAK FOR A TUMBLER
This trampoline artist has fractured
his lateral malleolus—his ankle.
In gymnastics even the slightest error in timing
can cause a powerful force to be exerted on
a bone at an awkward angle and produce
a painful fracture. This man's ankle will
be immobilized in a cast for eight weeks;
it should heal completely in 12.

pads of cartilage separating the vertebrae—may protrude and press agonizingly against a nerve. Or the fibrous tissue and tendon supporting the knee, ankle or wrist bones may stretch or tear, resulting in sprain.

Fractures, a classic affliction of the human race, occur so commonly that few people escape them. The very fact that bone is brittle makes it vulnerable to a break, especially through a blow or fall. Because men since time immemorial have tried to stop a fall with outstretched hands, the commonest fracture is a tipped-back break of the wrist, called a Colles's fracture after the 19th Century Irish surgeon, Abraham Colles, who wrote the first comprehensive description of its forklike deformity.

Happily bone, while susceptible to breakage, is also susceptible to solid mending, largely through its own efforts. The self-healing begins, in fact, at the moment of fracture, and in an orderly sequence of events. First, broken blood vessels at the fracture site form an enveloping blood clot, or hematoma. In a few days minerals from the sharp ends of the broken bone have been reabsorbed into the bloodstream, leaving the ends soft and rubbery. At the same time, connective tissue has formed cartilage, making a callus to hold the fracture fragments together. A fibrous lacing of additional connective tissue has grown through the hematoma, serving as a weak cellular glue to further secure the fragments. Within this sticky substance a special kind of cell, the osteoblast (literally, "bone-maker"), appears to strengthen the bone ends, depositing collagen, insoluble calcium phosphate and other minerals. In two or three weeks soft, calcium-rich new bone, or callus, shows on X-rays, bridging the gap between the bone ends. When the callus hardens, the mended bone can resume its job of weight-bearing and support. Often the healing is so complete that eventually the fracture site cannot be detected even by X-ray.

The process, however, takes time. Compared to torn skin, which may repair itself in days, or injured muscle, which may be ready for work again within weeks, bone may require months to heal. The deposit of enough calcium to strengthen and harden new bone is gradual. Bone cells grow and reproduce slowly. Blood supply to bone is relatively poor; as a result, when bone becomes infected its resistance is relatively low. All these problems are compounded, as in the case of the Snoqualmie Pass accident victim mentioned earlier, when a bone is broken into many pieces, or crushed out of shape, or severely displaced.

The orthopedic witch doctor

Before such bone can begin to heal properly, the fragments must first be returned to their proper anatomical positions, either by manipulation or surgery, and must be immobilized there by means of plaster casts, metal plates, pins, nails or screws. The basic technique of bone-setting has remained unchanged for centuries, although some doctors are now experi-

HEIGHT AND BONES
So precise is the relationship between various bones and height that anthropological detectives, with one dried bone as a clue, can closely estimate its owner's former living height. For example, if a 16.89-inch (42.9-cm) femur is found, the arithmetic table at right gives a living stature of five and a half feet (1.67 m). Interestingly, a radius that is long in proportion to the other three bones (as in apes) indicates a relatively short person.

LIVING STATURE (inches)					
MALE			**FEMALE**		
(2.89	× humerus)	+ 30.748	(3.36	× humerus)	+ 22.823
(3.79	× radius)	+ 31.268	(4.74	× radius)	+ 21.626
(2.32	× femur)	+ 25.799	(2.47	× femur)	+ 21.299
(2.42	× tibia)	+ 32.256	(2.90	× tibia)	+ 24.224
	1 inch = 2.54 cm				

menting with the use of electrical current to stimulate and speed healing.

By contrast with the ills that bone is prey to, its partner in the skeletal system—muscle—is, because of its exceptionally rich blood supply, the most infection-free of all the body's basic tissues. The muscular troubles most people are likely to encounter are of an everyday sort induced by strain or overuse. One of the commonest ailments is chronic myalgia, the muscle tension associated both with fatigue and with a state of undue alertness. Another is the soreness which afflicts us the day after we have overtaxed some portion of the anatomy beyond its ordinary exertions. The athletes among us occasionally suffer a bruised leg or thigh muscle as a result of a blow or forceful stretch; this is the condition which laymen label Charley horse, after the lame old nag who hauled the family surrey in the days before internal combustion.

A muscle for Mona Lisa

Like the bones, the skeletal muscles range in size and shape to suit the particular functions they perform. The muscles of the face, permitting a raised eyebrow, a frown or the faint smile of a Mona Lisa, are, some of them, less than an inch long; so are the muscles which unleash a lifetime of tongue-wagging. At the floor of the chest is the dome-shaped diaphragm, which is the main muscle involved in breathing, and is also involved in coughing, sneezing, laughing and sighing. In the neck and back, long, straplike muscles hold the head upright. The bulging, triangular deltoids of the shoulders raise the arms. The biceps and triceps of the upper arms bend—and unbend—the elbows. The broad pectoralis major muscles, those rippling signs of the he-man, move the arms across the chest. The massive gluteal muscles of the buttocks help us stand up and walk. The longest muscle in the body is in the thigh; it is known as sartorius, from the Latin for tailor, because it comes into play in the cross-legged position which tailors traditionally assumed. Sartorius and four bundles of muscles on each side of it called the quadriceps not only move the legs but also help us maintain our balance.

Whether large or small, the skeletal muscles can perform with prodigious speed and power. Such qualities can be literally of life-or-death importance, enabling the body to move in response to sudden and drastic changes in the external environment. Skeletal muscle can get into action within a few hundredths of a second, exert an enormous concentrated pull on the bone to which it is attached and, when necessary, support 1,000 times its own weight.

All muscle, visceral and cardiac as well as skeletal, moves by contracting itself—a unique characteristic which distinguishes it from any other body tissue. In the case of skeletal muscle, the individual cells, ordinarily long and thin, become shorter and fatter under stimulus and take on their tremendous pulling power. Once the stimulus has passed, the muscle relaxes, settling back into its original shape.

The precise nature of the process of contraction and relaxation—an extremely complex one both electrochemical and mechanical in nature—is still the subject of intensive research. It is known that a skeletal muscle contracts at the brain's command, responding to signals sent along nerves which are linked to muscle fibers. These signals spark a series of chemical changes in the muscle, converting chemical into mechanical energy, thus producing the actual movement of muscle contraction.

The strategy of two combs

A great deal more has been learned about the mechanical part of the process than about the chemical part. When the brain signals arrive at the junction of nerve and muscle, they penetrate deep into the tiny fibrils which compose muscle fiber. Each fibril, in turn, consists of rows of minute, filament-like protein molecules of two types, called actin and myosin. These face each other like two combs with their teeth partially interlocked. The muscle contraction takes place when the actin and myosin filaments glide toward each other as if to mesh. This action shortens the fibril, hence the muscle fiber, hence the muscle itself.

The chemical changes which bring the mechanics into play are as yet by no means fully understood. It is generally believed that one important such change occurs when the brain signals reach the nerve-muscle junction, which is located on the membrane of the muscle cell; a substance called acetylcholine, which acts as an excitant, is released, thus putting the muscle membrane on alert. The actual energy which the muscle needs in order to contract is supplied by the breakdown of a substance known as ATP (for adenosine triphosphate). This breakdown, in turn, is made possible by the conversion of glycogen, the powerful fuel which the body supplies to muscle in the form of glucose, a sugar. The muscle contraction itself is touched off by the release of calcium from a granular network called the sarcoplasmic reticulum. The calcium may also play a part in muscle relaxation.

If it is taxed repeatedly, without rest, muscle tires and ultimately stops contracting altogether. How long it can stay the course without faltering also depends, of course, on its basic health. The work a muscle does, or can do, is directly related to its size and its blood supply. Doctors who prescribe a daily dozen for their flabby patients are no Torquemadas in modern guise; exercise is vital if muscle tissue is to remain in good condition. Unless used, muscles tend to shrink and waste away.

In so doing, they deprive the body not only of its mobility but also of an important source of its heat. Few people realize that skeletal muscle helps keep them snugly warm, indeed sometimes too much so for com-

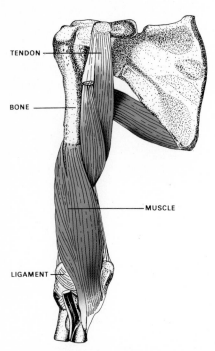

TENDON

BONE

MUSCLE

LIGAMENT

TEAMWORK IN THE LIMBS
Bone, muscle, tendon and ligament work together in an intimate relationship to move the body. Here, in the human arm and shoulder, bones give the limb its tensile strength and its basic framework, and are also busy centers for the manufacture of red blood cells. The limb is moved by skeletal muscles, which may be attached directly to the bone, or by tough connecting tendons. Ligaments prevent the bones from slipping apart at the joints.

fort. Of the energy released by glycogen, one of the body's fuels, only a quarter is used for muscular movement; fully three fourths burns off as heat. The more strenuous the activity, as in running, dancing or pushing the furniture around, the warmer we feel.

The great team of muscle and bone—aided by the connective tissue that holds them and other parts of the body together—has provided man, ever since he became man, with an unbeatable combination. We do not, by any means, know all there is to know about muscle and bone, and research continues into their makeup and behavior. Related to the studies of muscle contraction mentioned earlier, experiments have been performed in which the nerve ends connected to slow and fast muscle fibers are switched. Both types of fiber react to a brain signal with tremendous speed, but the slow fibers comparatively less so. Switching their nerve ends, it has been found, reverses the speed. Thus a whole new vista for exploration has opened up concerning the influence of specific types of nerve on muscle.

In the bone field, medical scientists have been evaluating the inorganic part of bone—the solid crystalline structure of the bone minerals. These crystals will absorb both beneficial substances, such as fluorine, and potentially harmful substances, such as radium or radioactive strontium from nuclear fallout, which belong to the same chemical family as calcium and can be absorbed in its stead. While the crystals will eventually reach a point of satiety, new mineral crystals continue to form throughout life, and to absorb small quantities of various elements.

Rescue of a sleepwalker

Through ever-improving surgical techniques, the replacement of both bone and muscle, when hopelessly injured or diseased, has met with increasing success. Muscle, tendon and bone can be transplanted, reattached or replaced in certain cases. Doctors have been able to split and effectively transplant leg muscles to substitute for ruined arm muscles. And the grafting of bone is no longer news. With bone grafts, surgeons can provide a scaffold upon which the patient's new bone can begin to grow.

In other notable areas of bone disability, neither animal nor human bone grafts have proved as satisfactory as out-and-out mechanical replacements. Knuckle joints crippled by arthritis are now supplanted by stainless steel or alloys such as Vitallium. Metal hinges—and specially molded rods—can often be used as permanent substitutes for hip, elbow and knee joints. Artificial knees equipped with mechanical devices that can imitate the motions of the human knee are especially beneficial for patients crippled with arthritis. And revolutionary artificial limbs that move when an amputee thinks about moving them are being developed with some success. The controls for the prosthesis may be attached directly to the re-

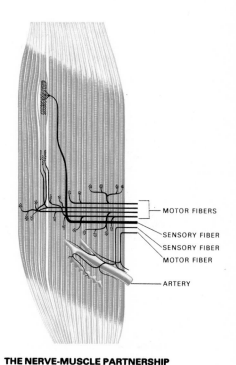

MOTOR FIBERS

SENSORY FIBER
SENSORY FIBER
MOTOR FIBER

ARTERY

THE NERVE-MUSCLE PARTNERSHIP
This highly simplified illustration shows a muscle and some of the nerve fibers that service it. Motor neurons—nerves that carry orders from the brain—branch out their fibers when they reach a muscle, and a neuron may control as many as 150 muscle fibers. Sensory neurons feed back information to the brain to be evaluated. The motor nerve fiber to the artery stimulates contraction of that vessel's muscular wall, thus controlling the blood flow.

maining nerves in the severed limb, and the electrical impulses transmitted from the nerves will make the new limb move. The success of all these operations stems from the body's tolerance of inert material.

Microsurgery, used in a wide variety of delicate operations, has made possible the effective reattachment of severed limbs and digits. Before the days of microsurgery, doctors could not reconnect the tiny, almost invisible nerves and blood vessels crucial to the full use of arms, legs, fingers and toes. Surgeons today, aided by microscopes, and sewing with fibers thinner than human hair, can reattach limbs that would otherwise be lost to amputation. Many patients who have had these operations—called replantations—regain at least partial use of their arms or legs.

For all the problems these developments imply, the remarkable fact about bone and muscle is how little trouble they give us. Almost every waking moment we subject them to a formidable amount of pounding and abuse. The average person walks some 19,000 steps a day—about eight miles. His muscles do an amount of daily work equivalent to lifting dozens of tons of wheat onto a wagon four feet high. Some machines, after only a few years of such treatment, would certainly become obsolescent. The body stands up to it for some three-score-and-ten years and still—at least insofar as its bone and muscle are concerned—may be little the worse for wear.

Triumphs of Structure and Design

Bone is the structural steel and the reinforced concrete of the human body. It supports the body the way a steel framework supports a skyscraper, and it protects its vital organs the way a cast-concrete roof protects a building's occupants. In filling these structural assignments, the human body solves problems of design and construction familiar to the architect and engineer. Among them are how to support a tower that cannot stand by itself, and how to build a protective covering that combines strength and lightness. To achieve its results, architecture uses a wide variety of materials—steel, aluminum, concrete; the skeleton uses bone only, but bone fashioned into a wide range of shape and size for a wide range of uses. Yet, the solutions are notably similar. It is not that architecture copied nature (much less the converse) but that, for given problems, the best solutions—in engineering as in the human frame—often are similar.

A SWINGING JOINT
Great demands are made upon the joint between the hip and the thigh: it must firmly support the weight of the upper body while standing, yet be flexible enough to allow leg mobility in many planes while moving. The effective solution is a ball-and-socket joint *(opposite)*. When similar flexibility is required, the same joint is used in devices such as the antennas built into TV sets.

64

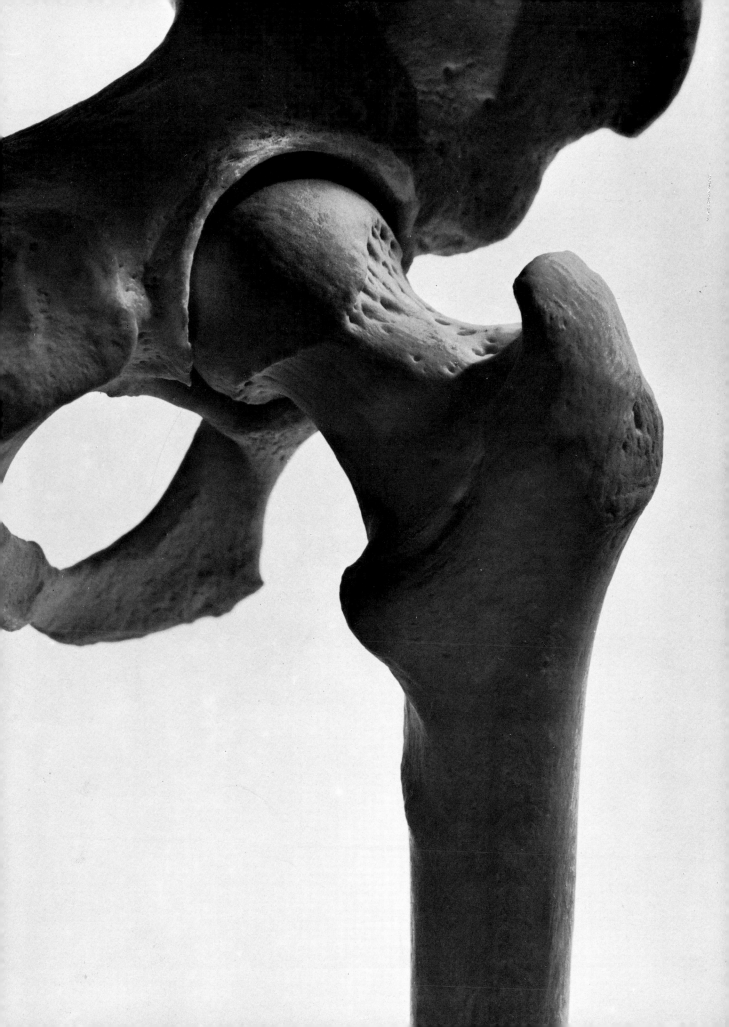

OKLAHOMA CITY TELEVISION TOWER

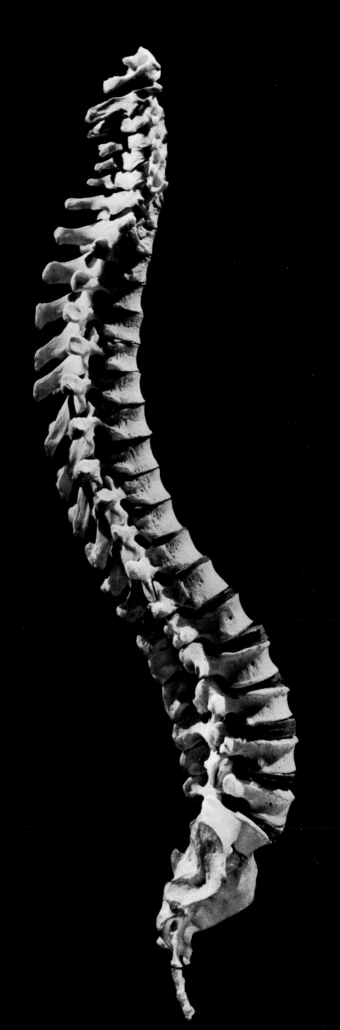

THE SPINE

Both structures shown on these pages would
be happier flat on the ground or floor. They
could not possibly stand by themselves.
To be upright they must be held in place by
elaborate systems of guy wires and supports.
On the opposite page is one of the tallest
man-made constructions in the world—
a TV tower in Oklahoma City. At right is
the human body's most central structural
member—the spine. The tower, 1,572 feet
(479 m) tall, would instantly collapse without the
web of steel guy lines which braces it against
the elements. Similarly the spine, a collection
of 26 articulated bones, must be held together
and kept upright by muscles and ligaments.
Among these are two straps of ligament
that run up the spine, front and back, to keep
it firm, and a pair of the body's largest
muscle masses, to keep the spine from
sliding. Atop the spine rides the head;
at the bottom the column is anchored in
the pelvis. Attached to it are the ribs;
running vertically through it are the trunk lines
of the nervous system, and at its very bottom
is the vestigial tail bone, or coccyx. The spine is
shown here in right profile and, of course,
without its supporting muscles and ligaments.

THE SPINE

THE CRANIUM

ROME SPORTS ARENA

68

THE CRANIUM

One of the most important duties assigned to the body's bones is to protect the brain. The eight thin pieces of armor plate which form the cranium, the brain's protective helmet *(opposite)*, meet at joints called sutures *(right)*. In children the sutures are not fused, but they become rigid splices when the child is grown. The mature cranium is much like a modern architectural form called thin-shell construction. The building shown below, fashioned by the Italian engineering genius Pier Nervi, is a graceful example of this construction. It uses a very thin layer of concrete which, because it is curved, is self-bracing and rigid; it is exceptionally strong for its weight—just as an eggshell is strong and light. The roof shell below has 1,620 small pieces; joined, they form a unit which, like the cranium, is designed to offer maximum protection for minimum weight.

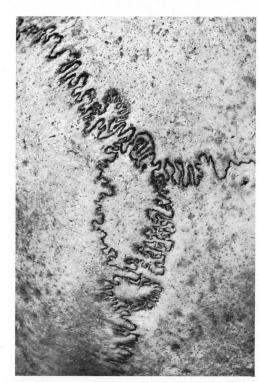

CRANIAL SUTURES

THE ELBOW

Man's most versatile tools are his arms—highly flexible extensions which permit him to reach out, grasp things and manipulate them. The arm's splendid utility is provided by a series of joints that allow it to bend, twist and turn. Most prominent of these is the elbow, a smoothly operated hinge between the carefully fitted bone endings of the upper and lower arm. At left is a triple-exposure photograph of the inside of the right elbow, showing the forearm bones straight out horizontally, bent up, and folded back toward the shoulder. Below, a lineup of five cranes demonstrates a man-made form of this flexibility. These cranes, too, provide access to out-of-the-way places—with their elbow joints. The chief difference is that the cranes work hydraulically, while the elbow is operated by groups of muscles and tendons—which at the same time make the human arm more shapely than a mechanical cherry picker.

MECHANICAL ELBOWS ON CRANES

THE ELBOW IN TRIPLE EXPOSURE

71

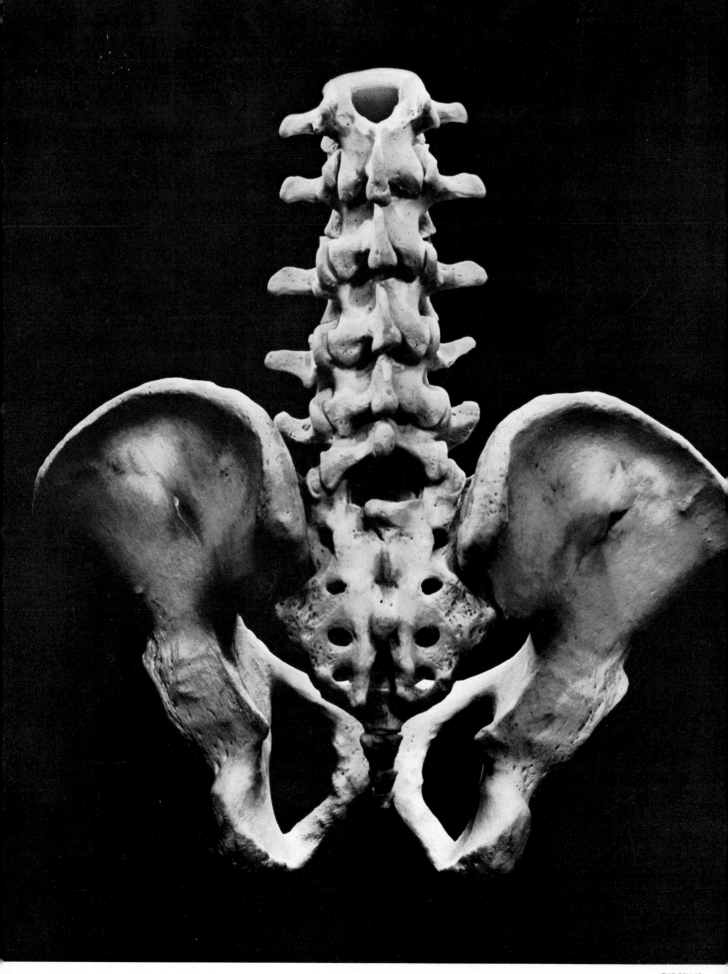

THE PELVIS

When a man stands, his entire weight is carried
by the bones of his legs down to his feet.
But when he sits, the weight is carried on
the two arches of bone *(opposite)* extending
below the flaring wings of the pelvis.
A seated person's weight is transferred to
the lower rims of the arches, areas known as
the ischial tuberosities. The arches are simply
and efficiently designed for taking the weight of
the torso as it is passed on by the spine.
The design is echoed in the building model
above. Here the weight of the roof is gathered
in sloping columns and carried to several
supporting points. All material unnecessary
for stress-bearing is removed and the result
is a light, open structure, called a space frame,
that provides a lot of solid support.

73

THE FEMUR

The strains placed on any supporting member, be it a floor or a bone, are never uniform. The curved beams on the underside of the floor below are placed to add strength only where the stresses occur. The cross-hatching of lines inside the bone on the opposite page does the same thing. The bone is the femur, or thigh bone, the longest and strongest in the body. The lines are ridges of bone built up in those planes where stresses occur. Should a fracture change the stresses (in the femur, they can be two tons per square inch [27,580 kPa], the living bone shifts its stress lines accordingly—a triumph of bone that buildings have never matched.

REINFORCED CONCRETE FLOOR

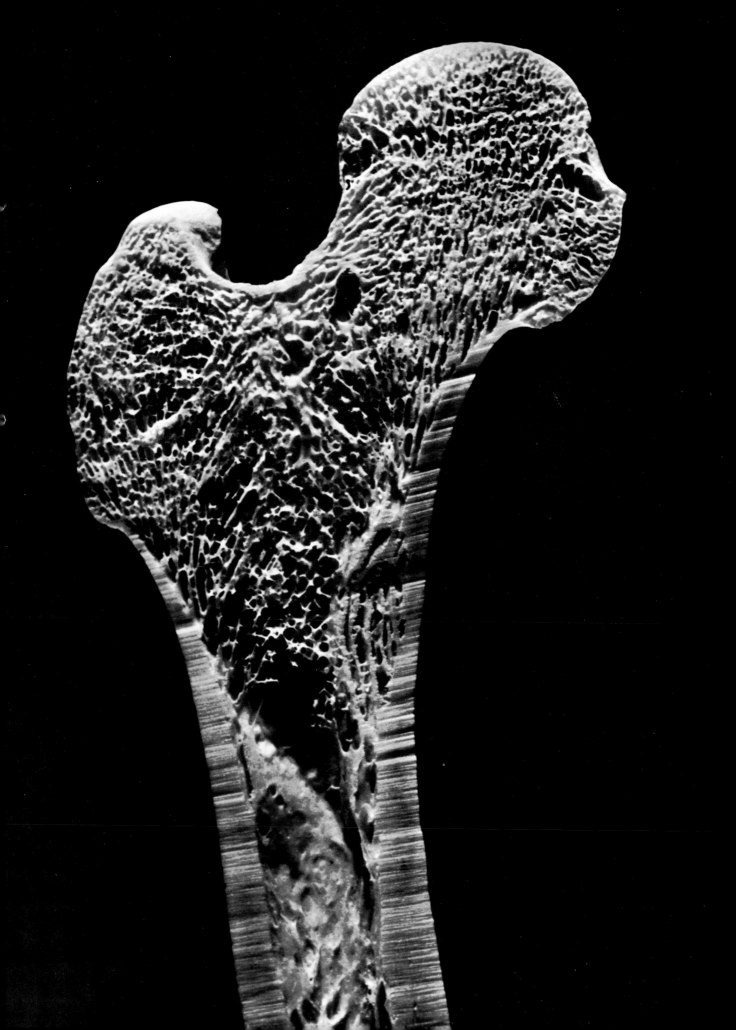

4
The Heart and Its Couriers

THE TEEMING TRAFFIC of the busiest metropolis presents a study in sheer inertia when compared to the ceaseless activity within our own bodies. Day and night, loading and unloading goes on at every one of the body's trillions of cells. Food and oxygen are taken on; waste products are taken off. The process slows somewhat during sleep, but it never halts. A stoppage would, indeed, signal death.

Like a great city, the body needs a transport system to carry its vital cargoes to and fro. This network—the circulatory, or cardiovascular, system—has its freeways, underpasses, cloverleafs, subsidiary roads, quiet streets and back alleys. In the nomenclature of the body, the lines of supply bear the labels of artery, arteriole, capillary, venule and vein. The total distance they cover, within the confines of the body, is estimated at 60,000 miles (96,500 km).

The major means of transport within this vast complex is blood. Its flow is controlled by the heart. Under impetus of the heart's pumping action, the blood, with its freight, makes continuous round trips, without pause, in and out of the heart, through the rest of the body, and back into the heart to be sent out again. The heart pumps so steadily and powerfully that in a single day it pushes the 10 pints (4.7 l) of blood in the average adult body through more than 1,000 complete circuits, thus pumping 5,000 to 6,000 quarts (4,730 to 5,680 l) of blood a day in all.

Even the earliest man was aware of his heart; he could feel it beat and pound. He also sensed that the red fluid spurting from a fresh wound was related to life and death. As sophistication grew, the heart and blood began to be associated. People amassed increasingly accurate data about the structure of the heart and blood vessels, but they still continued to guess wrong about the way the system performed.

The Greeks, for example, believed that the heart was the seat of the intelligence and of an "innate heat" that generated the body's so-called four humors—black and yellow bile, phlegm and blood. The last of the Greek medical luminaries, Galen, gave no credence to the notion that blood might circulate. As noted in Chapter 1, he preferred to compare the blood's movement to that of the tides. Once it flowed from the heart, Galen asserted, it ebbed back on occasion to dump its impurities, sometimes using the lungs for the same purpose.

Galen's pronouncements on the blood, as on other matters, were long regarded as inviolable. With slight modification, they persisted until a 17th Century Englishman, William Harvey, placed the affairs of the heart in proper perspective and gained medical immortality.

Research, reasoning and a bit of mathematical reckoning helped Harvey discover the mechanics of blood circulation. Bent on a physician's career, he went to study at the University of Padua. Italy was then under the spell of the great Galileo and his new principles of dynamics. Harvey began to

THE SURGE TO VICTORY
The stout heart of Herb Elliott, the Australian track star, makes it possible for him to drive to the tape to win a 1960 Olympics race *(opposite)*. In time of strenuous physical activity, the heart puts on its most spectacular performance. It pumps at a much faster rate than usual, in response to an immediate increase in the demand for blood by muscles involved in the exertion.

CHALLENGER OF GALEN'S GOSPEL
Galen said blood flowed back and forth like a
tide. But William Harvey *(above)* proved
with the experiment below that blood in veins
can run only one way—toward the heart.

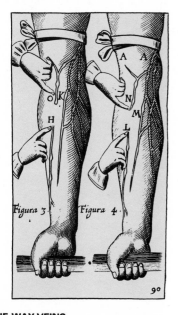

ONE-WAY VEINS
Harvey pressed blood upward from a vein
section. If he released his lower finger, blood
flowed into the section. But if he lifted his upper
finger, blood would not run backward.

wonder if Galileo's theories of movement might not also apply to the flow of blood within the human interior—a notable early example of the fruitful union of science and medicine.

Back in London, Harvey pursued his quest for more than two decades. He vivisected 15 different species of animals, examining the exposed heart and the way it expanded and contracted, and studying the arrangement of blood vessels. Harvey also experimented on living human beings, applying various pressures to those veins and arteries visible from the outside. When tightly bandaged, the veins would swell, but the arteries would not, and vice versa. He thereby confirmed their separate functions as incoming and outgoing channels for the blood.

A circle of blood

Harvey's crowning achievement was to prove that the blood circulated as a result of the heart's mechanical action. First he had to determine the volume of blood pumped by the heart. To do so he used Galileo's method for the quantitative calculation of moving objects. Working with the dilated heart of a cadaver, Harvey found that the most blood the largest section of the heart could hold was two ounces (57 g). He then figured that the heart beat 1,000 times every half hour, pushing a half ounce (14 g) of blood out with each beat. As it turned out, these figures were gross underestimates, but they nevertheless proved his point. According to Harvey's reckoning, the heart had to work over 500 fluid ounces (14.8 l) of blood every half hour. This was more than twice the blood in the entire body of a husky male. Manifestly, the heart had to be pumping the same blood again and again. "I began to think," Harvey wrote, "whether there might not be a movement, as it were, in a circle." He published his theories in 1628, in the classic *De Motu Cordis et Sanguinis* ("On the Movement of the Heart and Blood"). A startled medical world found them irrefutable.

Harvey was never able to pinpoint the place where the blood ceased moving away from the heart and began moving toward it. Four years after his death in 1657 the answer was found by the Italian physiologist Marcello Malpighi. Peering at the lungs of a frog under a microscope, an instrument not available to Harvey, he discovered the connecting links between veins and arteries—the capillaries, smallest of all blood vessels, so slender that 10 of them together are no thicker than a hair.

With the work of Harvey and Malpighi, the disarray of known fact about the circulatory system could be sorted out, and the picture we have of it today began to emerge more clearly.

The heart itself is no bigger than a good-sized fist. It weighs less than a pound (0.45 kg), and its shape resembles the popular Valentine image sufficiently to satisfy the sentimentalists. It lies, pointed downward, in the chest cavity, at about the mid-center body line. The walls of the heart are of thick muscle, twisted into rings, whorls and loops. Within them are four hollow chambers: a left and a right receiving chamber, or atrium, and below them a left and a right pumping chamber, or ventricle. In the right atrium is the sinus node—a minute blob with a mammoth job. Composed of special, nervelike muscle tissue found nowhere else in the body, the sinus node starts the heartbeat and sets its pace, much like the coxswain of a racing shell.

A solid partition of muscle, the septum, separates the left and right sides of the heart. Before Harvey, a stubbornly held misconception was that the blood moved through the heart by seeping through pores in the septum. The passages, however, open not from side to side but from top to bottom. These openings—with valves to control the direction of blood flow—connect the left atrium with the left ventricle, and the right atrium with the right ventricle. In effect, the heart is thus two pumps back to back. To get from one side of the heart to the other the blood must go the long way around, through the body.

Since the blood travels endlessly, an arbitrary choice must be made of a starting point to describe its route. Assume that a batch of fresh blood has just moved into the left atrium. At this point the heart is between beats—an interval of about three fifths of a second; it is only during this relaxation that the receiving chambers fill up. Then the atrium contracts, shoving the blood down into the left ventricle. As the ventricle contracts in turn, the blood is squeezed. This forces shut the left atrioventricular valve and forces open another valve which leads to the aorta, the body's main artery. Out into this surges the blood.

The ramifications of an arch

The aorta, about one inch (2.5 cm) wide, curves in a great arch—up from the heart, down along the backbone into the abdomen. From it other large arteries lead to the head, the digestive organs, the arms and the legs. From these branch the smaller arterioles, and from these the tiny capillaries, thousands of them in each of a countless number of networks—the last station on the blood's outward-bound journey.

Any fluid driven by a pump, and flowing in a circuit of closed channels, operates under pressure. The pressure from the heart is increased by muscles in the walls of the aorta; if the aorta were opened, blood would spout a column six feet (1.8 m) high. The large arteries therefore have tougher walls than do their branches—thick layers of muscle and elastic tissue with lots of give. The importance of this resiliency is perhaps best appreciated when the walls harden as a result of the deposit of fatty materials and calcium. This condition, with its coincident constriction of the artery channels, is known as arteriosclerosis, one form of which is atherosclerosis. Healthy arterial walls, however, stretch and rebound with

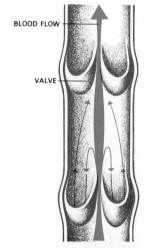

BLOOD FLOW

VALVE

VALVES TO REGULATE FLOW
If veins were simply tubes, blood would rush into a person's feet every time he stood up. The blood flow in most veins is regulated by valves—thin, membranous folds—that compel it to go in only one direction. When blood flows toward the heart, they allow it to pass. However, if the blood starts to go the wrong way *(small arrows)*, the valves fill up and stop the backflow. Defective valves allow the pressure of an unbroken column of blood from the heart to distend blood vessels in the legs, causing varicose veins.

each heartbeat. This movement is what we feel as the pulse, at any area of the body where the arteries lie close to the surface.

By the time that the blood reaches the capillaries it is moving at a relatively slow rate, along channels so narrow that its own cells, the corpuscles, must slither through sideways. Here the blood discharges its load of dissolved food and oxygen. These leak through the microscopically thin capillary walls, across a watery bridge which is provided by a fluid called lymph, and into the body's cells. Back into the bloodstream, by way of the same route, come carbon dioxide, urea and uric acid—castoffs from the cell. This brisk maneuver is executed in an area whose size may be judged by the fact that no capillary lies more than a hair's breadth away from a cell.

In yielding up oxygen and taking on waste, the blood turns color from bright to dull red. It now starts back to the heart, trickling from the capillaries into the venules—small veins—with which they merge. The venules converge into larger veins and then into the two largest, the *venae cavae*, just above and below the heart. The blood empties into the right atrium, descends into the right ventricle, then moves out through a large artery—the pulmonary artery—leading to the lungs. The lungs supply the blood with fresh oxygen and send it, newly scarlet and reinvigorated, to the left atrium, to start its round of the body all over again.

The entire intricate, tortuous process—from first to second entry of the left atrium—takes the blood the incredibly brief time of about 20 seconds.

Moreover, the general circuit of the body—the systemic, so called—is only one of several routes which the blood tirelessly travels. Its route to and from the lungs, described above, is known as the pulmonary circulation, and is regarded as the other major circuit besides the systemic. The systemic circulation also has a number of special divisions, local but altogether essential, around which the blood simultaneously zips to aid in the function of particular vital organs. These local circulations include the renal (to the kidneys), the portal (to the liver), the cerebral (to the brain) and the coronary (to the heart itself).

A case of supply and demand

Fast as the heart pumps the blood under ordinary circumstances, the speed is markedly stepped up in response to special demand from some part of the body. A commuter dashes for a train; his leg muscles instantly require an extra surge of blood. They get it, thanks to capillaries elsewhere in the body which temporarily close because their need for blood is not so urgent. The capillaries of the stomach and intestine pass up their usual helpings of blood quite often on such occasions; on the other hand, they are likely to be more demanding than usual after a meal, when their own capacity is taxed to help in the digestive process. It is for

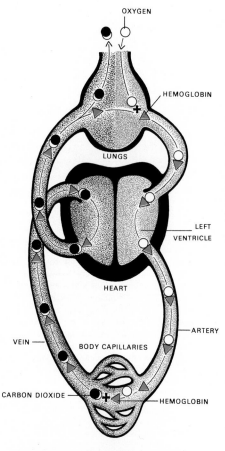

A TRANSPORT SYSTEM FOR THE BODY
The bloodstream is a vast transport system that carries oxygen to the tissues and brings carbon dioxide to the lungs to be expelled. Oxygen-laden blood is pumped from the left ventricle of the heart through the arteries and into the tiniest capillaries, where cells snatch up oxygen and turn over carbon dioxide to the red blood cells' hemoglobin. The blood flows back to the lungs, where the process begins again.

this reason that we can be drowsy or sluggish after a meal; the blood is going to the digestive tract instead of to the brain.

During strenuous exercise, heavy physical labor or any kind of stress, the heart may pump eight times as much blood as in a period of relative relaxation—as many as 12 gallons (45 l) a minute. To pump an equal amount of liquid, a hand pump considerably larger would have to work a lot longer. Yet the heart adapts to a short-term increase in work load without harm; it slows and rests when the demand falls off.

Even when the demand persists, the heart adjusts. Its muscles thicken, its chambers enlarge and it may actually double in size. The heart of a businessman with hypertension may fill half his chest cavity. In hypertension—high blood pressure—a variety of factors ranging from kidney malfunction to nervous strain may combine to create a resistance to the flow of blood through the arterioles, causing the heart to pump harder to surmount this obstacle. Whatever the cause, the heart, when forced into consistent overwork, pumps less efficiently. It tries to compensate by beating more frantically, until it cannot keep up, and fails.

A miracle cure for dropsy

A failing heart, however, can often be restored with almost miraculous dispatch by a potent chemical prepared from the common foxglove herb. The curative powers of this plant revealed themselves about 1776, through the ailing person of the principal of Brasenose College, Oxford. This gentleman suffered from dropsy—a waterlogging of the tissues in part due to heart failure—until he abandoned orthodox remedies and tried a homemade formula for dropsy, a special tea brewed by an old woman of Shropshire. The results were so astonishingly good that word spread. Analyzing the beverage, a compound of some 20 or more varieties of herb, a local doctor, William Withering, proved foxglove to be the active ingredient. Under its Latin name of *digitalis*, it has been one of the greatest boons to mankind in all the history of medicine.

The elements of blood itself have fascinated men ever since the microscope permitted a detailed look at them. One of the first to discover a blood component was Malpighi, not long after he spotted the capillaries which had eluded Harvey. Some 300 years later, for all the intervening refinements in detection techniques, many mysteries remain about the makeup of the blood and the functions of certain parts of it.

Blood has four main components. About 55 per cent of it is a fluid, plasma. The remaining 45 per cent is made up of three kinds of cells: red cells, or erythocytes, Malpighi's find; white cells, or leukocytes; and platelets, or thrombocytes. Except for one variety of white bloods cells, all the cellular components are manufactured in the bone marrow.

Plasma, in which the cells float, is a yellowish solution, 92 per cent water, the other 8 per cent a host of substances indispensable to life. Among them are nutrients—glucose, fats and amino acids; inorganic materials like sodium, potassium and calcium; special proteins like fibrinogen, albumin and various globulins; antibodies, defensive globulins which fight off viruses and other unwelcome intruders in the body; and hormones such as insulin and epinephrine, more familiarly known as adrenalin, which speeds up the heart rate whenever some emergency requires a greater blood flow to the muscles. With its potent arsenal to draw upon, plasma plays a crucial role in maintaining the body's chemical balance, water content and temperature at a safe level—a function quite apart from its role in the transport of food, oxygen and waste.

The red cells outnumber the white cells 700 to 1. Theirs is the exclusive and all-important job of picking up oxygen in the lungs, carrying it to the rest of the body and convoying waste carbon dioxide back the other way. Their life is hectic and short; after about three or four months they fall apart and are replaced by new recruits sent into the bloodstream from the bone marrow. The red cells' effectiveness as an oxygen-carrier is due to their content of hemoglobin, a compound of protein and iron which gives blood its red color. Hemoglobin has a chemical way of latching onto oxygen and holding it in its grip until its destination is reached. Because oxygen does not dissolve well in plasma, the binding power of hemoglobin is vital. Otherwise the blood could carry only enough dissolved oxygen for two and a half seconds, and any period of breathlessness, such as the brief time after a sneeze, might well prove fatal. When, for any reason, the hemoglobin content dips below minimum body needs, the result is anemia, meaning, although not quite literally, "no blood." A diet deficient in iron-rich foods, such as meat or eggs, may cause anemia in the robust as well as the frail.

A rally of wrigglers

The white cells constitute the blood's mobile guard. Some are endowed with the curious ability to wriggle out of the bloodstream and back in again. They rally in great numbers wherever invading bacteria gain entry into the body, engulfing and destroying them. Whenever white cells mobilize for action, the body compensates by manufacturing more. Double the usual number may appear in the blood within hours. Often this rising white count, as doctors describe it, serves as an early tip-off to dangerous infections.

Perhaps the strangest of blood's three cellular components are the platelets, named for their resemblance to tiny plates. For a long while these cells, discovered about a century ago, utterly baffled researchers. Then it was observed that people with low platelet counts were very vulnerable to bleeding. Platelets were found to be vital to blood-clotting.

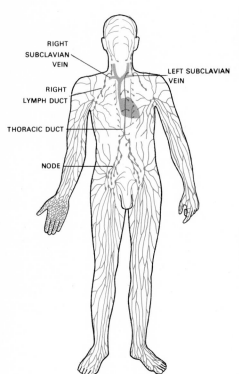

RIGHT SUBCLAVIAN VEIN
LEFT SUBCLAVIAN VEIN
RIGHT LYMPH DUCT
THORACIC DUCT
NODE

LYMPH SYSTEM IN A MAN

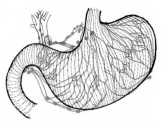

LYMPH VESSELS SERVING THE STOMACH

THE BLOOD'S DRAINING SYSTEM
Throughout the body there is an extensive network which carries lymph. The lymph vessels collect waste-bearing fluids which have seeped through blood-vessel walls, and return them to the bloodstream via two main lymphatic ducts emptying into two subclavian veins near the heart. The lymph nodes—enlarged tissue masses in the lymph vessels—are filtering devices for removing bacteria and other foreign matter.

When they touch the roughened surface of a torn blood vessel, they burst apart, releasing chemicals that set off a reaction in the blood leaking out. The exact steps are still in dispute, but the result is the conversion of one of plasma's proteins, fibrinogen, into a network of crystals that enmesh the red blood cells—thereby forming a clot which seals the leak.

In its basic operations blood finds a powerful ally in the substance known as lymph. This watery fluid, as mentioned earlier, serves as a bridge across which oxygen, nutriments and wastes pass between the capillaries and the body cells. As the bloodstream unloads its offgoing cargoes through the capillaries, many of its plasma proteins—fully half of them in the course of a day—also escape, under the force of blood pressure. Once they have broken out, the errant proteins cannot get back directly into the bloodstream. The lymph, therefore, takes a hand. It convoys them—via a special circulatory system of its own, composed of lymphatic capillaries and ducts—into veins near the shoulders, which pass them into the heart. Lymph also carries along a number of chemical products, including droplets of fat and cholesterol which are absorbed during the process of digestion. By the time the meandering and relatively sluggish lymphatic system brings these cargoes back to the heart, they have been greatly diluted.

The first transfusions

The performance of the lymph, and of the blood itself, has been largely revealed within our own century. Today, for example, it is commonplace knowledge that an individual possesses either blood type A, B, AB or O. But it was only in 1900 that the existence of various blood types was established; the discoverer was an Austrian physician, Dr. Karl Landsteiner, who later won the Nobel Prize for his work. His research was the inevitable outcome of centuries of trial and error in blood transfusions. The transfusion technique was a probable offshoot of the early custom of drinking blood as a means of rejuvenation; the Romans, for example, would rush into the arena to quaff the blood of dying gladiators. The first transfusion on record was effected in 1667, by Jean Baptiste Denis, physician to Louis XIV of France. Denis temporarily restored a dying boy by injecting about eight ounces of lamb's blood into his veins. In time, transfusion attempts became more widespread. But why some worked, and why some failed, or even proved fatal, was a question that continued to perplex doctors until Landsteiner.

The simple technique which Landsteiner used was to mix, in test tubes, the plasma of one person with the red cells of another. In some cases the two blended smoothly; in others, the cells would not mix, clumping together instead. Inside the body such clumping would clog the capillaries—a dangerous and perhaps deadly situation. The key to clumping or not

PERCENTAGE OF WATER IN TISSUES

Fat	20
Blood	80
Bone	25
Connective	60
Kidney	80
Liver	70
Muscle (Striated)	75
Skin	70
Nervous Tissue:	
Gray Matter	85
White Matter	70

THE HUMAN RESERVOIR
If it were possible to drain all the water from a 160-pound (72.6-kg) man, his dehydrated body would weigh a mere 64 pounds (29 kg). This table shows where much of the body water is distributed. There is no more water in the blood than in some so-called "solid" tissues. Turkish-bath habitués will be chagrined to learn that there is less water in fat than in any other tissue, including bone.

clumping, Landsteiner found, was the way red cells containing a particular protein, or agglutinogen, reacted to plasma containing another type of protein called an agglutinin. Red cells with one type of protein would be compatible with plasma containing one type of agglutinin, but not with plasma containing another type.

Landsteiner accordingly typed human blood as A, B or O (for zero). The red cells of this latter type contained no agglutinogens at all, and could thus provide a blend with any type of plasma; hence a type-O person became known as a "universal donor." The next year, two other researchers, one a pupil of Landsteiner, found a fourth blood type, AB, whose plasma would receive any type of red cell; hence a type-AB person became known as a "universal recipient." In 1940, four decades after his original discovery, Landsteiner, now deceased, discovered in collaboration with the late Dr. Alexander S. Wiener a new substance in the red cells which they labeled the Rh factor, after the rhesus monkey whose plasma they mixed with human red cells.

The perilous Rh factor

It was found that when a mother who lacked the Rh factor, and was thus "Rh-negative," gave birth to a baby who was "Rh-positive," the infant would be born with serious brain damage or would sometimes die. This situation does not usually arise with the first child, but results from any portion of the first pregnancy that is traumatic to the fetus. In such cases, the mother's blood mixes with that of her baby to create antibodies that can cause birth defects in future babies. Recently, however, vaccines known as Rh-immune globulins have been developed that, when administered within 72 hours of delivery, prevent the mother from reacting to the Rh-positive red cells of her next baby. Thus by suppressing a mother's natural immune response to her own child, doctors can ensure that Rh-positive babies of Rh-negative mothers will have a normal chance for life.

The same kind of progress has attended the treatment of heart defects—an area where some of the breakthroughs have been as controversial as they have been spectacular. The first shock wave was touched off in 1929 by Werner Forssmann, a young German doctor. Forssmann had previously passed a thin rubber catheter through a vein in the arm of a cadaver into the heart. Then, in an experiment so hair-raising colleagues regarded him as a lunatic, he decided to try this on himself. His first attempt failed; the doctor assisting him lost his nerve. Forssmann repeated the effort alone, as a nurse stood by. With fluoroscope and mirror, he followed the catheter's progress as he moved it up the vein in his own arm. When he had inserted the tube 20 inches (51 cm), its tip entered his right atrium. But he knew no one would believe what he had done without unassailable evidence. With the catheter still in place, he walked down a long corridor and up two

A TRANSFUSION, 1667
In the first known successful transfusion of blood to a human, Jean Baptiste Denis, a 17th Century French physician, drained lamb's blood into the arm of a boy suffering from fever. When the boy revived, Denis tried it on another patient, as shown in this 1667 print. The patient reportedly went directly to a tavern to celebrate; he died shortly thereafter. Both Church and state outlawed transfusion and a century passed before it was tried again.

flights of stairs to have X-rays made as proof of his achievement.

This extraordinary experiment was reported in an obscure journal. It went unheeded until two Americans—Dr. Dickinson W. Richards and Dr. André Cournand—recognized in it the diagnostic technique that heart surgeons needed, and developed it into commonplace procedure. Subsequently they and Forssmann jointly received the Nobel Prize for their work.

Although this technique provided the means to pinpoint the location and extent of heart damage, the idea of approaching the heart with a scalpel was still awesome. Indeed, at that time so great was the fear of starting massive bleeding or causing the heart to stop that surgeons did not dare to enter the heart. Research, of course, was not at a standstill. What the surgeons were looking for was a way to empty the heart of blood so that they would have a "dry" field in which to work.

A stand-in for the heart

Finally, in the late 1940s, the problem was met by the invention of the heart-lung machine, whose workings are illustrated on pages 130 and 131. Hooked up to the patient's circulatory system, this machine shunts the blood away from the heart, oxygenates it artificially and pumps it back into the general circulation—while the surgeon does his repair work without interruption.

Once open-heart surgery had become a reality, all manner of other operations came to be added to the surgical repertoire. By far the most celebrated of these was the transplanting of a human heart, the first case of which is described on page 134. If there was ever a feat that captured the medical mind, this was it. Suddenly scores of doctors throughout the world began performing the operation and within the course of a year, medical teams had done no less than 99 transplants in 17 different countries. At first the results were dismal; most of the patients lived less than three months. Today, 70 per cent of these patients live at least a year after the operation—a rate that compares favorably with that of patients who have received kidney transplants.

While not as drastic, another feat of anatomical shuffling involves grafting sections of veins from the patient's own body onto the heart to reroute blood around clogged arteries. Although this coronary bypass, as the surgery is called, has been performed on tens of thousands of people suffering from angina—the severe chest pains caused by arterial blockages—it is still the subject of a great deal of debate. Most of the patients who have had the operation swear by it, as do many doctors. But some heart specialists believe that conventional drug therapy may be just as effective as a means of relieving the pain, and as a means of prolonging the patient's life as well.

Beyond such differences of opinion, however, development of new and better methods of treatment continues. One of the most remarkable is a procedure for patching a hole in the wall of the heart—without open-heart surgery. It consists of running two small umbrella-like patches via a catheter through a network of veins to the heart. Once inside, the first umbrella is extended, pulled back against the opening and locked in place by the second opened umbrella.

A similar advance has been made in repairing damaged heart valves. From the plastic valves that were first used in the early 1960s, surgeons have moved toward greater use of pigs' heart valves, which reportedly involve fewer irritations in the blood and far less clotting than their synthetic counterparts.

Today no aspect of the circulatory system escapes the exploratory eye of the medical scientist and technologist. Spurring their efforts is the awareness that some of the most basic questions about the circulatory system remain unanswered. We do not yet know precisely what causes high blood pressure, hardening of the arteries and heart attacks. The part played in the onset of such ailments by the celebrated cholesterol—a fatty substance carried by the blood—is yet to be settled. We are far from sure of the origin of some blood cells. Indeed, we do not know why the heart itself beats. Enough mystery still hovers about the circulatory system to preoccupy legions of heart researchers for decades to come.

Blood, Circulation— and Life

Among all the body's systems, the blood is unique: it is the only fluid tissue. This fluid, endlessly coursing from the heart to the remotest parts of the body and returning, is a sea in which the body is bathed. Every cell is an island that could not exist without the blood and its derivative lymph, which surround it. Pumped by the heart (opposite), the blood delivers the food and the oxygen that combine in the cells to produce energy; then it carries away the waste produced by the cells. It carries off excess heat generated by the internal organs to be dissipated through the skin. It distributes the regulatory hormones that govern, among other things, the internal chemistry of the body. And it delivers the agents that fight disease and those that rebuild tissue damaged by disease or accident. The safe transfer of blood and its vital qualities from one person to another has been among the most important developments of modern medicine.

A FIST-SIZED PUMP
The endless circling of the blood depends upon one tireless muscle: the heart (opposite). Though it is only about the size of the fist and weighs a half to three quarters of a pound, the heart does enough work each day to lift the body a mile straight up. In this frontal view of the organ, an injection of pigment gives color to the web of veins, arteries and capillaries that serve the heart.

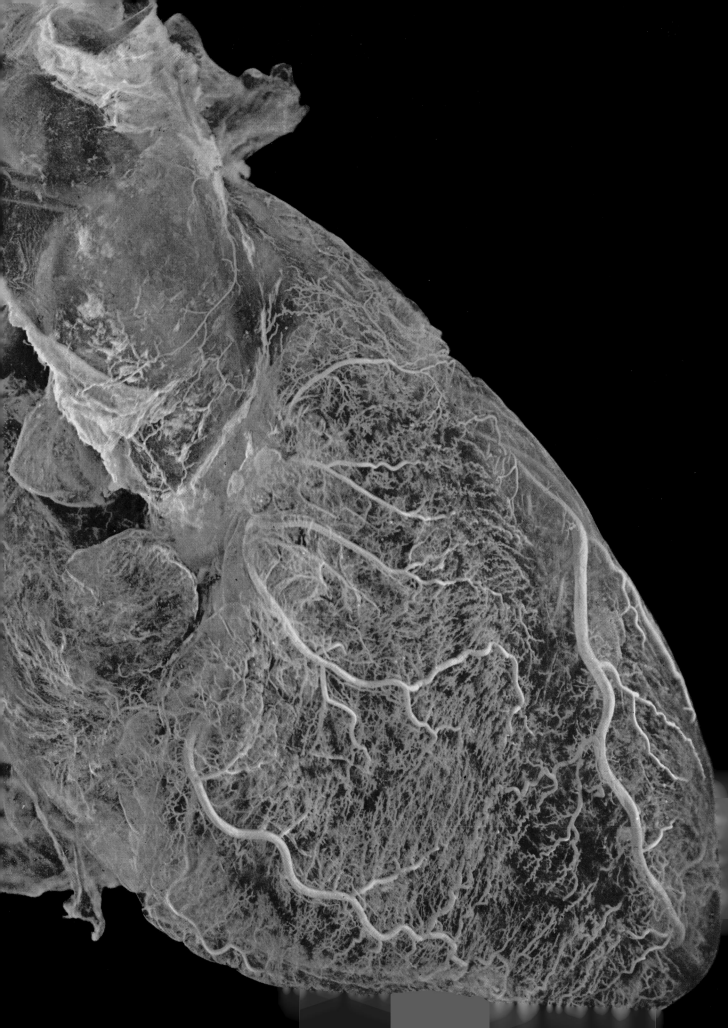

The Blood Vessels, Large and Small

The raw materials for the energy that powers man's every thought and action are transported in the blood. The enriched blood is carried in a network of tiny vessels, capillaries, to each cell. These capillaries are so small that 60 long ones or 120 short ones would stretch only the length of this line of type. Yet there are so many capillaries in the body that, laid end to end, they would ring the equator more than twice.

Blood coming into the capillaries from the arteries has been loaded with oxygen in the lungs or with food from the digestive system. The walls of the capillaries are only one cell thick, so thin that the nutrient-laden blood is able, by osmosis and diffusion, to pass its oxygen and food to the body's cells and to receive from the cells their waste. The spent blood then flows from the capillaries into the veins, which direct it back to the heart. In the heart the blood enters the arteries and is carried by them to the lungs and digestive system, to be aerated and enriched again before returning to the capillaries.

The body's largest blood vessels, the aorta and the pulmonary artery, are about an inch in diameter. Arteries have thick elastic walls, the pulsations of which assist the heart in pumping. Vein walls are more rigid. Many of them, particularly in the lower part of the body, have valves which prevent a backflow of blood.

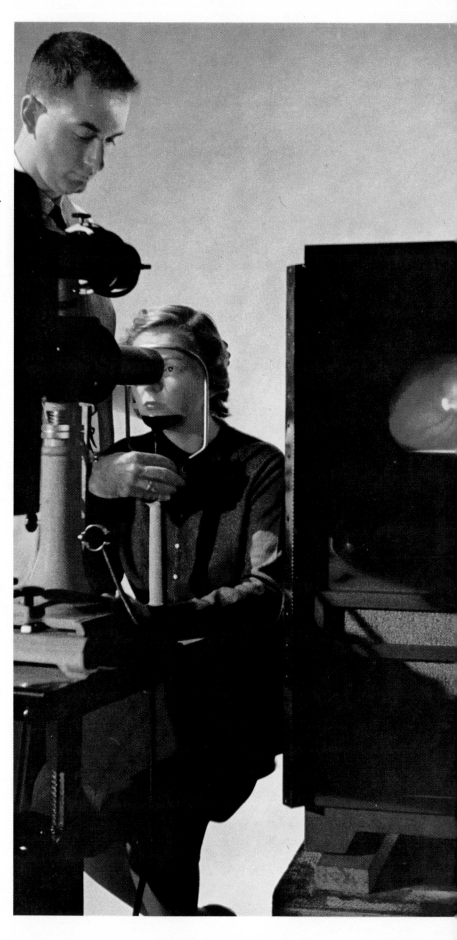

AN INNER VIEW
A television camera photographs the retina of the eye through an opthalmoscope and projects the image on a screen *(right)*. Thus, the eye provides a window for examining the flow of living blood inside the body. The retina, the innermost layer of the wall of the eyeball, shows orange on the screen; the blood vessels appear as red and the optic nerve is seen as yellow.

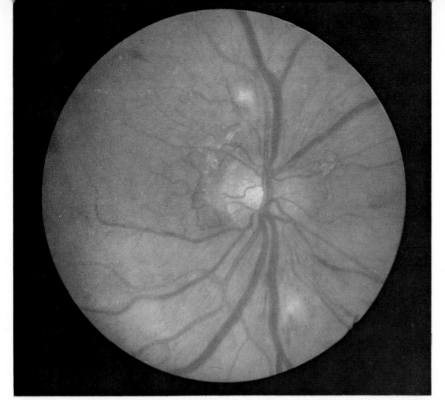

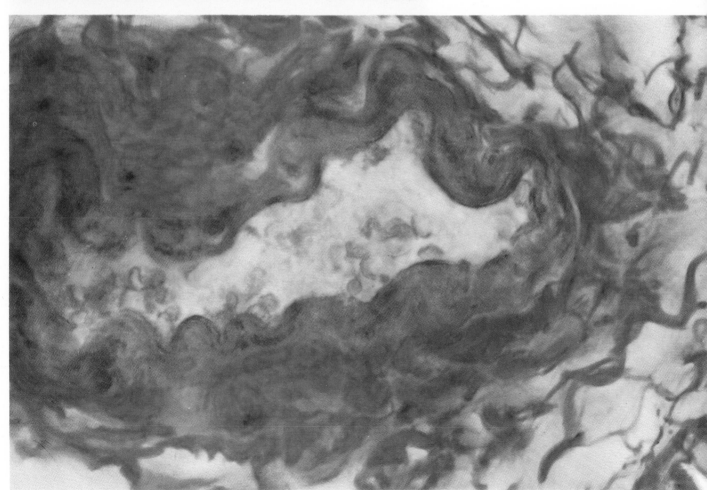

A MUSCULAR TUBE
This cross section of a venule, or small vein, shows its inner layer of elastic membrane in brown and its muscles in red. In the living organism the blood would flow in the irregular, flattened hole in the center. The cross section has been enlarged 250 times. Venules collect blood from the capillaries and carry it to even larger veins which transport it to the heart.

89

A State of Mutual Dependency

Blood is indispensable to every cell of the body. The need for its vital supplies is so universal that even blood vessels have blood vessels. Blood sustains even those organs by which it is, itself, sustained—the heart, the stomach, the lungs, the intestines.

The stomach *(right)* helps to prepare the food that the blood carries to all parts of the body. After the food has been reduced to particles that are small enough to enter the bloodstream, it is received by the blood through the permeable walls of the villi *(lower right)* which line the inside of the small intestine.

The lungs *(below)*, which have the densest congregation of capillaries of any part of the body, load oxygen into the blood. The blood, in turn, releases in the lungs for exhalation the waste carbon dioxide it has received from cells everywhere in the body.

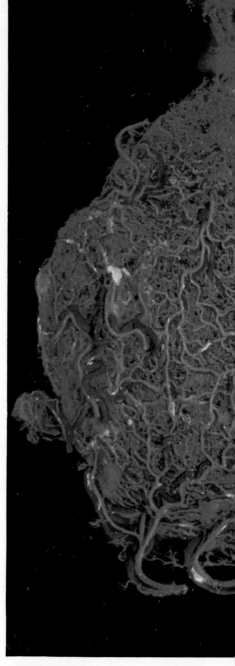

THE STOMACH
A mass of blood vessels supplies the stomach *(above)* with nutrients. The larger arteries *(red)* and the veins *(blue)* occur in mutually entwined pairs. The smaller capillaries, through which the stomach's cells receive the food and oxygen they need to live, also are shown in red.

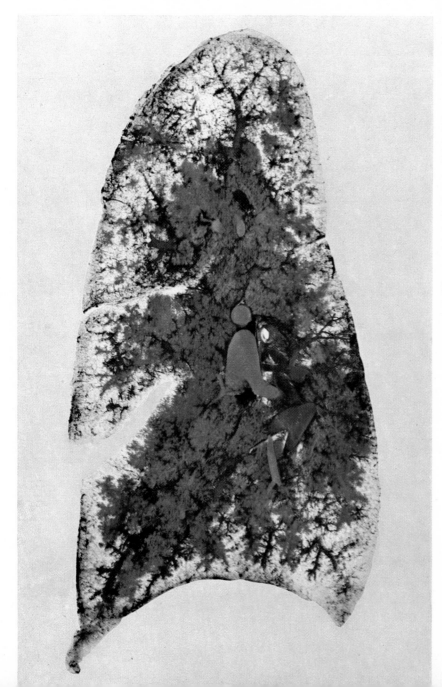

THE LUNGS
Bright red capillaries cover a human lung *(left)* like clumps of moss. The larger arteries and veins are shown in red and blue respectively. Each lung has about 375 million alveoli, or air pouches. Capillaries largely compose the walls of the alveoli and take fresh oxygen from them.

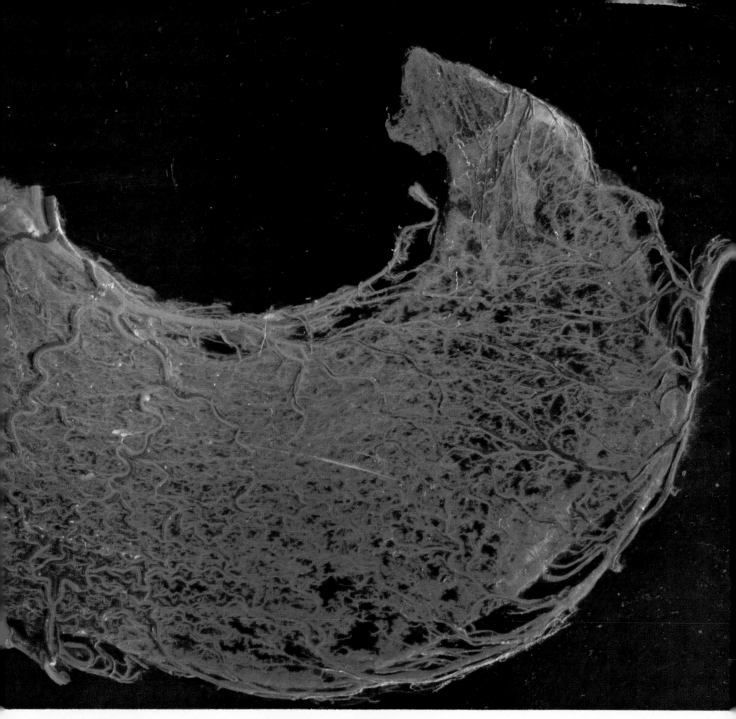

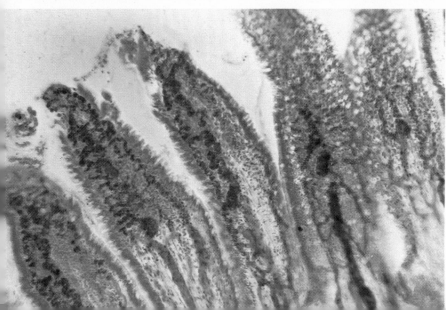

THE INTESTINE
Villi of the small intestine *(pink)* pass nutrients from the digestive system to the blood vessels *(blue).* These tiny fingers extending into the intestine are shown here magnified about 100 times. They increase the absorptive surface of the intestine to about 30 square yards (25 m²).

THE OXYGEN CARRIERS

Red corpuscles (salmon-colored at right) cluster in a blood sample. Carriers of the blood's oxygen, these cells are not capable of moving themselves but are swept along by the flow of the blood, frequently stacking up like plates. They are manufactured in the marrow of bones.

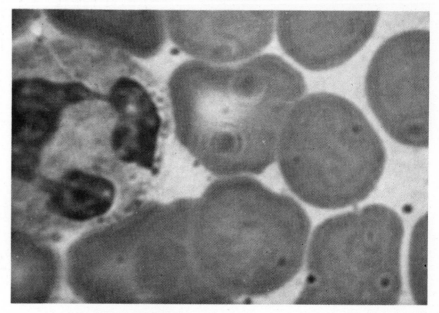

THE FIGHTING CELLS

White corpuscles are stained violet in the photograph below. Unlike red corpuscles, white cells have a many-lobed nucleus that may appear fragmented under the microscope. When pursuing bacteria, they can move with or against the bloodstream. A red cell on edge between two white cells appears at upper left.

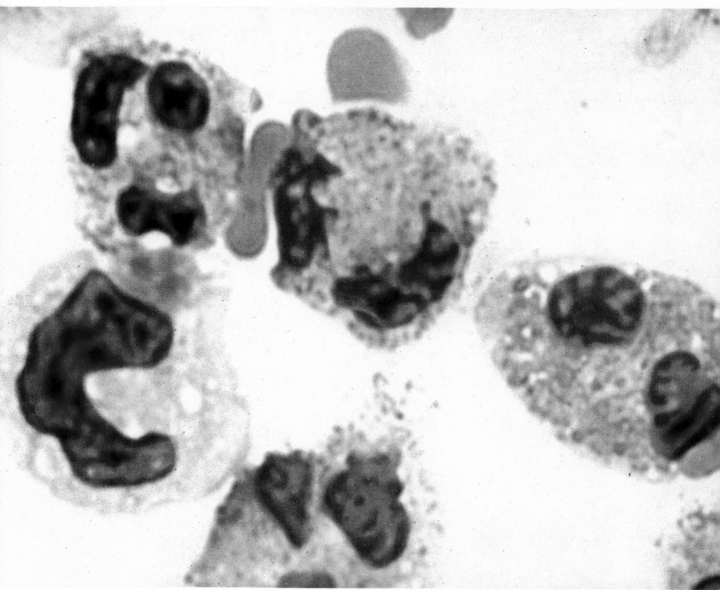

10 Pints of Vital Fluid

The blood teems with life. Billions of cells float about carrying oxygen, repairing leaks and fighting bacteria. In the average man, about eight million blood cells die each second and are replaced by new cells produced in the bone marrow, lymph glands and lymphoid tissues of the tonsils, spleen, thymus and intestine.

The blood cells swim in the plasma, which also transports food, antibodies, hormones, clotting agents and wastes. Plasma is practically all water and makes up just over half the blood's volume. In an average man with 10 pints (4.7 l) of blood, about five and a half pints (2.6 l) are plasma.

Red corpuscles *(opposite, above)*, 25 trillion of them, occupy about four and a half pints (2.1 l). These cells contain hemoglobin, an iron compound which can pick up more than half its weight in oxygen. They start with a diameter of perhaps nine 10,000ths of an inch (.0023 cm), shrink at maturity to three 10,000ths and break up after about four months.

White cells *(opposite, below)* and platelets make up the remaining volume of the blood. Platelets, which live only for two to four days, outnumber the larger white cells by 1.5 trillion to 35 billion, but are so small they fill only two teaspoons. Their tendency to adhere to whatever they touch fits them for the job of repairing leaks. The white corpuscles fight infection by eating bacterial invaders *(below)*.

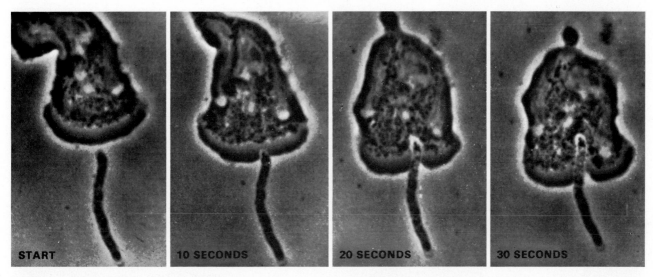

START   10 SECONDS   20 SECONDS   30 SECONDS

A white corpuscle begins to attack a bacillus that threatens the body with disease. Ten seconds later it starts to ingest the invader.

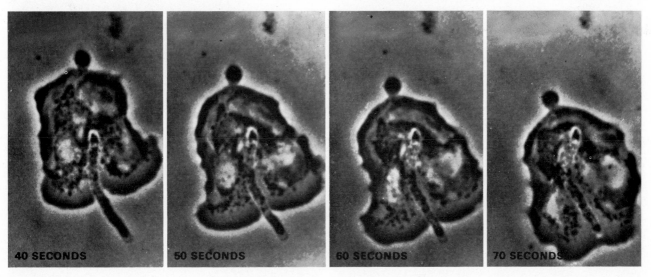

40 SECONDS   50 SECONDS   60 SECONDS   70 SECONDS

Within 70 seconds the white cell has completely absorbed the attacker. The microscopic engagement is here enlarged 2,000 times.

The Rich Mine
of Blood

When blood is needed for treatment of a patient, the parts are sometimes greater than the whole. With a centrifuge *(opposite)*, medical technicians can separate a unit of whole blood into components. The red blood cells, for example, can then be used to treat patients who suffer from severe anemia, or the platelets can be used to help those with leukemia.

Plasma—blood with all the cells removed—provides still other useful products. And these derivatives, which are extracted by methods pioneered in the 1940s by a Harvard researcher, Edwin J. Cohn, also combat specific conditions.

Normal serum albumin, for example, fights shock by preventing hemorrhage. Gamma globulin, carrying antibodies that attack viruses and bacteria, confers upon the recipient, at least temporarily, the donor's immunity to measles and certain kinds of hepatitis or infantile paralysis. Antihemophilic factor provides a blood-clotting mechanism that is missing in some males.

The usefulness of these agents is heightened by the fact that they can be frozen *(overleaf)* or powdered and stored for months. And because technicians are able to select the components to be removed from the blood, the rest can be returned to the donor *(below)*, thereby eliminating the waste that is involved in extracting whole blood or plasma unnecessarily.

HOPPER OF HELP
With his ears muffled against laboratory noise, a technician wearing sterile garb empties a centrifuge of a pasty protein fraction extracted from plasma. To preserve them for later use in transfusions, such blood derivatives are then stored in special cold-storage rooms, where the temperature is kept at −5° C. (23° F.) or colder.

SEPARATING THE SPECIFICS
The blood processor below can collect large amounts of platelets from a single donor in 1½ hours. The donor's whole blood is pumped into a bowl rotated by a centrifuge, where the platelets are separated from the other components and diverted to a collection bag. After the platelets have been collected, the plasma and red blood cells are returned to the donor.

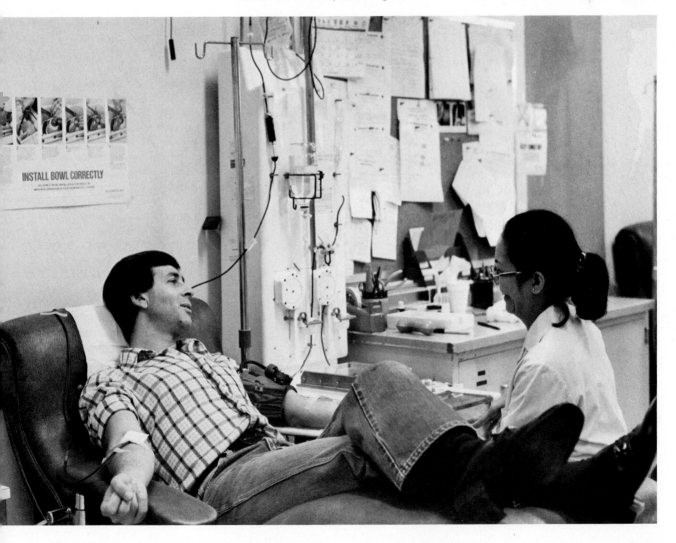

INSTALL BOWL CORRECTLY

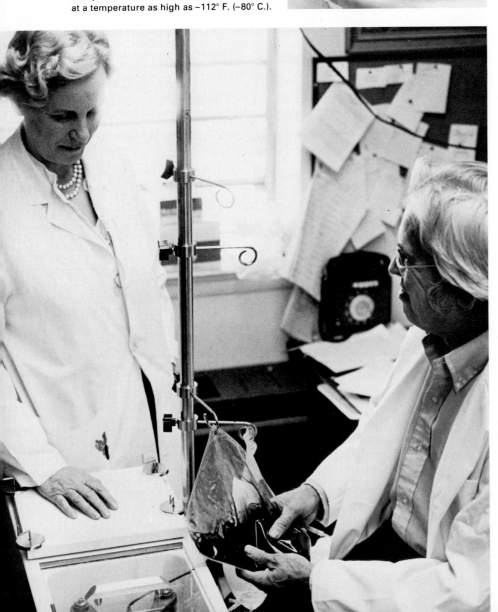

The Red Cells and Flash Freezing

There was a time when blood could not be preserved for more than three weeks. At the end of this "21-day tyranny," as the storage period was called, the red cells had so aged outside the body that they were no longer suitable for use in transfusions.

Eventually, an answer to the problem was found in the techniques of cryobiology (from the Greek, *kryos*, meaning icy cold). The Reverend Basile J. Luyet, a Swiss-born priest working at Saint Louis University, found in 1949 that he could preserve 70 per cent of the cells of ox blood by dropping its temperature to –202° F. (–130° C.) in a second's time. As other scientists followed and began freezing human blood, they found that the cells' water content could be supplemented with glycerol, which freezes without forming ice crystals that can rupture the cell membrane.

Cryobiologists currently preserve whole blood by using methods like those shown here. In each procedure the basic technique remains essentially the same: The red cells are filled with glycerol, put into special airtight plastic bags, and then immersed in liquid nitrogen or frozen in special refrigerators. Prior to their use in a transfusion, the cells are washed in a solution of salt or sugar to remove the glycerol. So effective is this process that blood thawed out after more than 10 years of storage cannot be distinguished from freshly frozen blood.

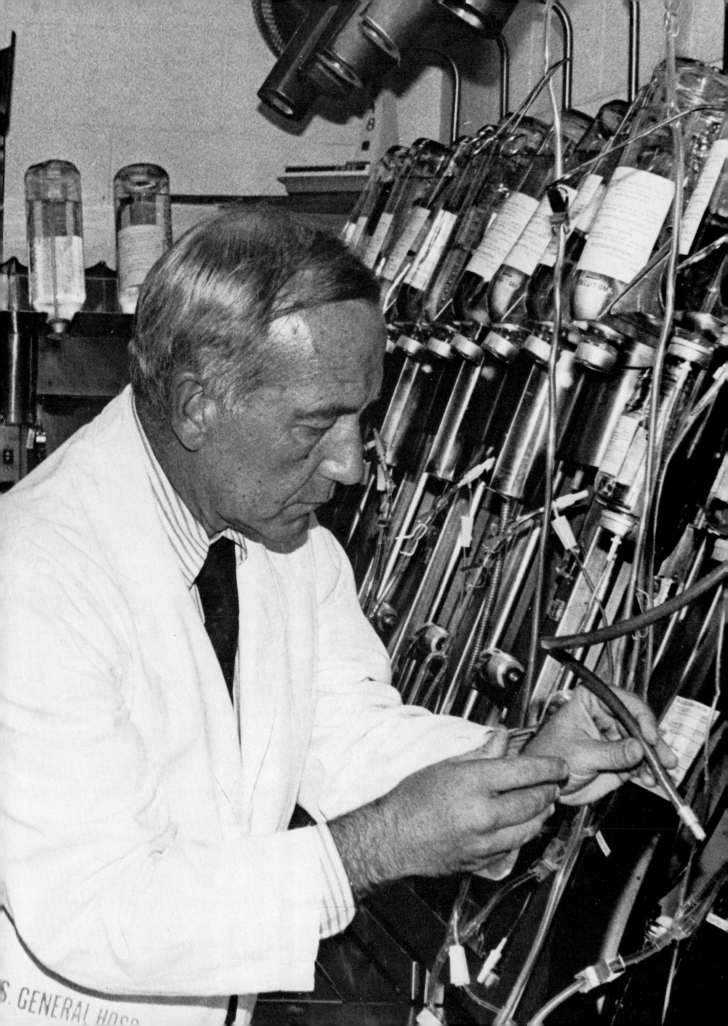

5
Fueling the Body's Machinery

MORE THAN CAN BE ACCURATELY MEASURED, medical advance has hinged on individual case histories. Down through time many men and women have contributed to the mainstream of our knowledge of health and disease through maladies privately endured and often not overcome. For the most part their identities are beyond recall. Among the rare exceptions is Alexis St. Martin, a 19th Century French-Canadian fur trader who was destined to provide posterity with its first real insight into the human digestive system.

One June day in 1822, at a trading post on the Michigan-Canadian border, St. Martin was struck by an accidental shotgun blast which tore a great gaping hole in his left side. William Beaumont, a young Army surgeon, arrived from nearby Fort Mackinac to treat him. Certain that his patient would not live more than about 36 hours longer, Beaumont dressed the wound as best he could. But St. Martin, who was 18 years old at the time, survived and healed, although a tunnel two and a half inches (6.4 cm) around remained open in his side, leading directly through the skin and muscle into the stomach. When he had fully recuperated, he was able to resume his usual vigorous pursuits, simply protecting his wound with layers of gauze.

St. Martin's fistula (false opening) was not unique in history. A similar case had been reported as far back as 1530. Beaumont, however, was the first doctor to realize that the fistula could be used as a peephole to watch the digestive system in action—a process hitherto hidden to the eye. With astonishing persistence, lacking a laboratory or skilled help, he made a number of investigations of inestimable value to his profession ever since.

Long before Beaumont, physicians had realized that food, once it had been taken in, had to undergo radical transformation before it could be utilized in sustaining the body. They knew that it was chewed and ground in the mouth, and lubricated by saliva. They also knew that it passed from the throat into the stomach by way of a narrow, 10-inch-long (25-cm) channel called the esophagus, from the Greek word which means "to carry what is eaten."

But what happened once the food reached the stomach? For centuries, popular belief held that it simply putrefied there. The first hint of the real answer came in the early 1700s. A French scientist, René de Réaumur, performed a series of experiments with a pet bird—a kite—which led to a major revelation. Kites have the protective habit of regurgitating anything they cannot digest. Réaumur lowered tiny pieces of sponge into his bird's stomach. When they came up, he found that they had absorbed a juice so potent that, as test-tube trials proved, it would dissolve bits of meat into liquid. His discovery persuaded physiologists that digestion was initiated by a secretion produced inside the stomach. But

CORNUCOPIA MIDWESTERN-STYLE
Harvest-time helpers join a Kansas farmer at a noonday dinner of fried chicken, cranberry sauce, pickles, potatoes with gravy, chocolate cake and fruit. Although the metabolic system might be expected to quail under this onslaught, the rugged labors of these diners help them burn off the fuel into which the food is converted, and permit another large meal by nightfall.

no one had the opportunity to observe the stomach at work until St. Martin had his accident.

Beaumont's excitement was reflected in his notebooks. "When he lies on the opposite side," he wrote, "I can look directly into the cavity of the Stomach, and almost see the process of digestion." One of Beaumont's techniques was to attach pieces of food to a length of thread and lower it, through the fistula, into the stomach. By withdrawing the food when it was partly digested, he confirmed that the stomach did, indeed, secrete a powerful digestive juice. By further painstaking studies, Beaumont was able to draw some 50 "inferences," as he called them, about the gastrointestinal system, among them that the stomach acted in exactly the same way no matter what the diet, that bulk as well as nutriment was necessary in food intake, that "stimulating condiments" were harmful to the stomach, and that "the use of ardent spirits always produces disease of the stomach, if persevered in."

A twisting trip down the GI tract

The conclusions which Beaumont drew about the way food passes through the body provided the guidelines for the extensive research which inevitably followed. The path of the food lies along the gastrointestinal tract—GI tract for short—a channel so coiled and twisted upon itself that it winds and bends for almost 30 feet (9 m) from the top of the esophagus to the anus. Like other natural functions, such as the coursing of blood through the veins or the healing of a broken bone, digestion proceeds without any direction on our part. We may consciously decide to chew or not to chew, but we seem unable to influence the activity of our salivary glands. As the food is swallowed—mainly by reflex action—it passes altogether beyond our control. Automatically, muscular contractions triggered by the act of swallowing close off three possible routes the food might take: back into the mouth, up into the nasal cavity or into the windpipe. Only one route is left open—down the esophagus and into the stomach.

Food requires no help from gravity to make its way down the coiled pathway; an astronaut's digestive system works very well indeed in a condition of zero gravity. The motive power is furnished by muscles which stretch the full length of the tract. They form two layers, one running along the tract and the other encircling it in concentric rings. Both by setting up a churning motion, and by a series of progressive contractions which are known as peristaltic waves, the twin sets of muscles force food all the way from the throat to the rectum, much as if toothpaste were being squeezed along its tube by some built-in power contained in the tube walls.

Most people believe that their stomachs are situated near their navels.

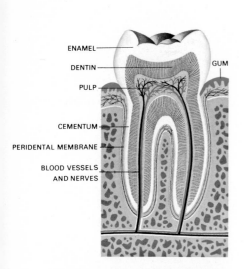

A HUMAN MOLAR IN CROSS SECTION
The exposed portion is called the clinical crown and is covered by enamel, the hardest substance in the body. Below the gums, the root is covered with softer cementum. Beneath the layer of bonelike dentin is the pulp, which houses the nerves and blood vessels. The tooth is attached to the jawbone by the peridental membrane, a tough connective tissue.

ENAMEL
DENTIN
PULP
GUM
CEMENTUM
PERIDENTAL MEMBRANE
BLOOD VESSELS AND NERVES

In fact, the stomach lies much higher in the abdomen, on the left side, nested up under the diaphragm and protected by the rib cage. In form, it is a kind of pouch, about 10 inches long, with a diameter that depends on its content. When it is full, it can stretch to hold as much as two quarts (1.9 l) of food. When it is empty, it collapses on itself like a deflated balloon.

The processing which food undergoes, once it has been eaten, is a rugged one. It is conceivable that there might be fewer gourmets, and fewer cases of obesity, if the digestive process were visible, or if its clinical detailing in television commercials were more closely heeded. A hurriedly gulped tunafish sandwich on rye bread and a slowly savored beef à la Bourguignonne meet the same inexorable fate: whatever the food, it is mashed, churned, pulverized and generally battered beyond recognition. But it is only by these gyrations that the digestive system manifests its efficiency, and ensures our physical energy, our freedom from potentially noxious wastes and, indeed, even our repeated ability to indulge in the joys of the appetite.

Whether slated to be converted into energy or to be eliminated as waste, ingested food materials take the same route along the gastrointestinal tract for five sixths of the way. Arriving at the entrance of the stomach from the esophagus, the food has already been softened. Its entry into the stomach—as well as its exit therefrom—is regulated by circular muscles which act somewhat like purse strings, alternately expanding and contracting. The stomach itself works on the food both mechanically and chemically. The movement of the stomach walls mashes it further, kneading it as a cook kneads dough. This also permits the thorough mixing-in of a digestive juice whose chief ingredients are pepsin and hydrochloric acid.

The role of the enzymes

Pepsin is one of at least 700 varieties of enzymes which are known to exist in the human body. Each of these complicated organic compounds has its own particular task to perform, but all of them function as catalysts to speed up chemical reactions. Some enzymes help break down foods, and others have many nondigestive duties. Without enzymes, in short, bodily functions would proceed far too slowly to enable them to sustain life.

Dozens of different enzymes participate directly in the digestive process alone. Among them, pepsin serves to break down the protein in food in the stomach. It can act, however, only in the presence of the hydrochloric acid, which assists in the preparation of the food for digestion. Hydrochloric acid is such a strong corrosive that it will eat its way straight through a cotton handkerchief, yet it does no harm to the stom-

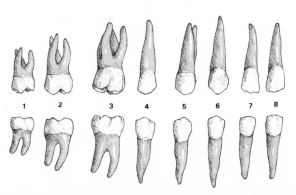

TEETH AND THEIR JOBS
These teeth are the right-hand half, upper and lower jaws, of an adult's set of 32, which gradually push out a child's 20 milk teeth between the approximate ages of six and 17. The adult can chew up nuts and meat with his molars (1, 2 and 3), grind food for swallowing with the premolars (4 and 5), rip into skin with his canines (6), and nip off a stem and nibble into the cheek of an apple with his incisors (7 and 8).

101

ach walls. A film of sticky mucus, lining the walls, protects them from being damaged by the acid.

All this activity represents only one function of the stomach, however. Its principal role is as a storage tank where food can be kept until the next section of the GI tract, the small intestine, is ready to receive it. The small intestine processes food in very small quantities at a time. To prevent it from becoming overwhelmed, food is allowed into it under control of the circular muscle located at the lower end of the stomach—aptly labeled pylorus, the Latin for "gatekeeper." It is the action of this muscle that enables us to eat large meals several hours apart; otherwise we would be forced to nibble small snacks at brief intervals. By expanding and contracting, the pylorus keeps the small intestine properly supplied with food.

The small intestine is the longest section of the GI tract, twisting and coiling for more than 20 feet (6 m). Here the essential chemical reactions which break food down begin in earnest. The first section of the small intestine is the duodenum, 10 to 11 inches (25 to 28 cm) long. This segment received its name from the Latin word for "twelve," owing to the fact that its span was originally measured by 12 finger widths. In the duodenum the hydrochloric acid in the food arriving from the stomach is neutralized by alkaline digestive juices. Some of these juices are supplied by the pancreas, a soft, pink gland which lies below and behind the stomach; some are supplied by the liver, the heaviest organ in the body, a dark red gland which is situated below the lower right side of the rib cage.

Running the intestinal gantlet

Once the acid has been neutralized, the chemical breakdown of food moves into high gear. As the food is forced along the duodenum, it is like a person running a gantlet. It undergoes constant bombardment; any scrap that happens to escape one assault runs into another one farther on. The attackers are the most powerful of all the digestive enzymes. By contrast, the impact of pepsin in the stomach, or of preceding enzymes in the mouth, is minor. Indeed, a person whose stomach has been removed by surgery can still manage to satisfactorily digest food if it has been properly chewed. But the stoppage of enzymatic action in the duodenum could be critical.

Once through the duodenum, the battered food particles face final disintegration. This takes place in the second and third sections of the small intestine, the jejunum and the ileum. There, tiny, soft, hairlike projections called villi protrude from the mucous lining of the small intestine like nap from a Turkish towel. Named for the Latin for "tuft of hair," the microscopic villi extend the total area of the intestine and greatly aid the course of digestion. At the base of these minute structures are the crypts of Lieberkühn, openings to the intestinal glands which secrete more enzymes—in the form of intestinal juice—necessary for the last phases of digestion. Proteins in the food are broken down by the enzymes into amino acids; carbohydrates into the sugar molecules glucose and fructose; and fats into fatty acids and glycerol. Moving ceaselessly like ocean waves, the villi speed the absorption of the now-digested foods, in soluble form, into the body.

Waste ingredients such as cellulose—a fibrous component of raw fruits and vegetables that humans cannot digest—are forced on into the colon, or large intestine. Serving as a vast, nubby filter, the villi wave the waste through to the rectum and, by a series of final peristaltic contractions, from the body.

While the villi are dispatching the waste one way, they are sending the beneficial amino acids, sugars and fats other ways. The fats move into the special circulatory system described in the previous chapter, the lymphatic vessels, which send them into the bloodstream to be diluted, and thence to go wherever needed in the body. The amino acids and sugars are passed along the capillaries of the blood through the great portal vein into the liver, there to be converted into a form usable by the cells of the body.

The liver's primacy as the chemical capital of the body was intuitively suspected long before it was actually confirmed. Through the ages many powers have been ascribed to the liver. It was thought to be the seat of the soul, of love, of desire and of courage. It was also believed to produce yellow bile, one of the body's "four humors" which were supposed to determine health and disease; when bile was the dominant humor among this quartet, the person who was the occupant of the body in question was presumed to be hopelessly bad-tempered.

Safety in a surplus

The liver does, indeed, manufacture bile. It is also, by far, the most versatile of all organs in the body, so indispensable that without it the body would perish within 24 hours. In addition to its part in the digestive process, it filters old red cells from the blood; it acts as a general detoxifier for the body, removing chemicals and drugs taken in from the outside; it manufactures other complex chemicals needed by the body, such as blood proteins and cholesterol; and it synthesizes lipids—a kind of fatty material—which, among other functions, help form insulating sheaths about nerve fibers. As if to compensate for the rash placement of so many eggs in one basket, the body is provided with a vast surplus of liver tissue. We can limp along reasonably well if as little as a fourth of the liver is performing normally. Moreover, it has remarkable recuperative qualities; when one part is damaged, it tends to grow new cells to replace the lost ones.

In the digestive process the liver's role is in the nature of a follow-up. All the way down the GI tract, the digestive process consists of breaking food down. In the liver the process is reversed. The sugar is built up into a new substance, a special body fuel called glycogen. The sole function of glycogen is to provide a convenient and compact form of storage for glucose, which, in its own form, would take up too much room. As the body requires additional nourishment, the liver reconverts the glycogen to glucose, releasing it, a little bit at a time, into the bloodstream. In this way, the liver is also responsible, in part, for maintaining the level of sugar in the blood.

Parallel to the processing of sugar in the liver, another vital transformation takes place with the amino acids, the fundamental units of protein. These are rearranged into the body's building blocks, for continuing use in the regeneration of its cells. Every part of the body enjoys this service, and with impressive speed. The lining of the entire GI tract itself, for example, is renewed every three days. The blood carries the converted foodstuffs to the body's cells, which transform them into both structural units and energy. It is this transformation which is the ultimate goal of the digestive process.

The "gut hormones"

There are a vast number of gastrointestinal hormones produced by different parts of the GI tract that perform a variety of specialized functions when they are stimulated. These hormones, released in differing amounts, can either aid or thwart digestion. One of these intestinal hormones is histamine, only recently discovered in the GI tract though long known as a substance elsewhere in the body. Histamine is synthesized in the gastric mucous membrane, producing gastric secretions, especially acids. Doctors have found that by inhibiting the production of histamine in the intestines, they can reduce the quantity of acid in the GI tract of ulcer patients, and so lessen their discomfort. Somatostatin, another hormone newly discovered in the GI tract, is also a product of the gastric mucosa. It is believed to inhibit the release of gastric juices and of hydrochloric acid. Some scientists believe somatostatin may also inhibit the release of insulin from the pancreas in response to changing blood glucose levels, and so they are studying its relationship to diabetes.

Much is still to be learned about these so-called "gut hormones." But it is known that the process of digestion in the small intestine and of the elimination of wastes by way of the large intestine—in fact, the entire procedure by which foods are broken down into useful nutrients, useful fluids and useless wastes—is controlled by involuntary release of gut hormones.

THE MIRACLE OF METABOLISM
The remarkable process by which all cells convert food into energy *(below)* or prepare it for storage for later use *(opposite)* is shown here in simplified drawings. During conversion, or oxidation, fatty acids, amino acids and glucose are ground down by enzymes. After nitrogen wastes in the amino acids are eliminated, the rest undergoes a cycle of combustion, named for its identifier as the Krebs cycle. From this it emerges in the form of carbon dioxide, water and the energy needed for the body's work.

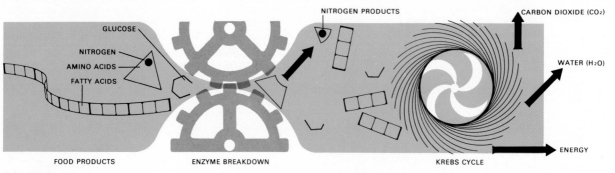

GLUCOSE · NITROGEN · AMINO ACIDS · FATTY ACIDS · NITROGEN PRODUCTS · CARBON DIOXIDE (CO₂) · WATER (H₂O) · ENERGY

FOOD PRODUCTS · ENZYME BREAKDOWN · KREBS CYCLE

Scientists are discovering a connection between these gut hormones and the hormones secreted by the pituitary, at the base of the brain. The digestive system works without any conscious intervention, yet its enormously elaborate mechanism is coordinated and controlled by the nervous system. This is done through a complex network of nerve cells that relay messages back and forth between the GI tract and the brain. Ordinarily we do not, by an act of will, interfere with this relay system. But through it, without our ever being aware of the fact, the digestive machinery can be heavily influenced by the reactions induced by emotions such as anger or fear, tension or insecurity.

The existence of a relationship between the emotions and digestion has been known for centuries. The dry mouth or the empty sensation at the pit of the stomach caused by fear, the heavy stomach that accompanies depression, the cramping pain of tension—these are sensations which all of us have shared. Beaumont, that indefatigable observer, noted that anger and excitement produced physical changes in his patient's stomach, the lining becoming "sometimes red and dry, at other times, pale and moist." But it was not until the early 1940s that a detailed, systematic investigation was carried out to trace the precise physical effects which emotional reactions can bring on in the digestive tract. As with Beaumont, the doctors who made this second historic investigation were able to do so as the result of an accident which left its victim with a fistula into his stomach. Unlike Beaumont, they did not have immediate access to the victim; almost half a century elapsed before they even encountered him.

The clam-chowder chronicle

In 1895 a nine-year-old boy, memorialized in medical chronicles simply as Tom, swallowed some steaming-hot clam chowder under the impression that it was beer. The chowder seared his esophagus and blocked it off from his stomach. Tom was rushed to the hospital, where repeated efforts to unblock his esophagus failed. It was then decided to perform a gastrostomy—an operation to provide an artificial channel from the outside into the stomach which would permit the burned esophagus to be bypassed and yet allow Tom to feed himself. While he was on the operating table, however, his condition suddenly became critical, and the surgeon was forced to finish the operation hurriedly, without attempting to devise a closure. The boy pulled through, but was left with an opening into his stomach an inch and a half wide.

Tom's fistula came to be the dominating factor in his life. He learned how to digest his food by chewing it up and then spitting it into a funnel that was attached to a rubber tube that led directly into his stomach. He ate only twice a day, and he had to allow a period of five hours

STORAGE FOR THE FUTURE
The cells, no wastrels, use food not converted into immediate energy to repair and rebuild worn tissues, while the excess is thriftily stored. Both call for the conversion of food products into tissue. This aspect of metabolism, called synthesis, is diagramed below. On the left hand are fatty acids, amino acids and glucose, plus glycerol with carbon. On the right, these products are shown after they have been re-formed by a cell into the body's complex substances —fats, proteins and carbohydrates.

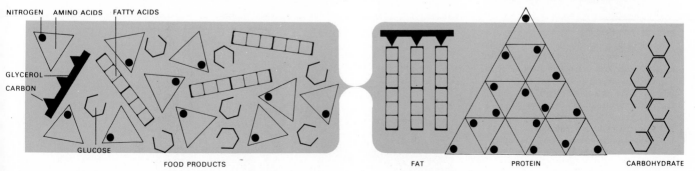

NITROGEN AMINO ACIDS FATTY ACIDS

GLYCEROL
CARBON

GLUCOSE

FOOD PRODUCTS

FAT   PROTEIN   CARBOHYDRATE

before he ate another meal, until his stomach was empty; otherwise, the food would spill over. Tom soon found that he was able to cope with these physical difficulties. But he was in constant fear of embarrassment and of ridicule.

For more than 30 years, Tom contrived to keep his fistula a secret, even from doctors, and to engage in strenuous manual labor. Then one day in New York, in 1939, while he was working as a ditchdigger, lifting a heavy pick every few seconds, the steady movement of the pick caused the bandage over his fistula to rub against it, making it bleed. Weakened by the loss of blood, Tom just barely made his way to a hospital. There the case of the muscular little man came to the attention of two doctors. Immediately they realized that within their grasp was exactly the same kind of extraordinary opportunity which Beaumont had seized more than a hundred years earlier.

Beaumont and his 19th Century successors had concentrated on the physical processes of digestion. Like many of their contemporaries, Tom's doctors were more interested in tracing the effects which various emotional states can have on the body. In particular, they were eager to discover whether prolonged emotional disturbance could lead to serious damage to the stomach.

An emotional stomach

At first Tom was reluctant to cooperate; it took the two doctors several months to win his confidence. Their discoveries more than justified the wait. In repeated experiments, they found that certain of Tom's emotional reactions regularly triggered the same physical reactions. When he was feeling aggressive or resentful, his stomach reacted as if it were preparing to receive a meal—though in fact he had a distaste for food at the time; it secreted digestive juices, and the capillaries in the lining filled with blood, transforming it from its usual pink to a rich red. When Tom was sad, fearful, depressed or withdrawn, exactly the opposite effects occurred. The acid secretions decreased and the stomach lining became bloodless and pale. Normally, even if a person is not hungry, the introduction of food into his stomach will, through physical contact, stimulate the usual set of digestive responses. But whenever Tom was really depressed, food had no effect on his stomach at all.

It is worth noting that Tom's feelings, either of anger or of sadness, could occur both when he was hungry and when he was not hungry. In short, while emotional reactions trigger physiological reactions, these in turn may or may not affect appetite. Some people, much as they need food, are unable to eat when depressed. Others gorge themselves as if to distract their minds from their misery. The experiments with Tom showed that if an emotional reaction is strong enough, it can sometimes

SMITTEN BY COLIC
The 19th Century caricaturist George Cruikshank, in a portrayal of a woman seized by colic, shows her screaming as grotesque dwarfs throttle her midriff. "Colic" is a generic term for an abdominal pain which can be caused by a number of conditions, including the intake of irritating or indigestible foods—or simply by overeating.

completely overcome the body's need for food. At other times it can speed up or slow down the digestive process. When Tom was angry or anxious, and his gastric juices were overactive, he might digest a meal in four to five hours instead of the usual five to six. When he was depressed, food might remain undigested in his stomach for many hours.

Through their experiments, his two doctors confirmed what had long been suspected: that emotional reactions can cause too much acid to be produced by the stomach. Whenever some of this excess escapes from the stomach—carried up the esophagus with a gas bubble or down into the duodenum with the food—those sections of the digestive tract which lack a protective lining suffer accordingly. Hyperacidity can cause the relatively minor annoyance of heartburn or it can seriously aggravate a peptic ulcer.

Ulcers across the ages

Peptic ulcers are not an exclusively modern complaint. "When there is an ulcer in the stomach or bowels," wrote Paul of Aegina, a prominent Byzantine physician of the Seventh Century A.D., "the patient must abstain from all acid food or drink." This recommended remedy almost suggests that Paul had guessed one of the principal hallmarks of ulcers: the excess acid which can be induced by sustained overactivity of the stomach. In some cases, the amount of acid secreted may be twice that needed for digestion. Without food to neutralize it, the acid may chew away at the sticky mucus which protects the lining of the stomach, at the lining itself, or at the walls of the duodenum. The victim may receive warnings, as the ulcer develops, in the form of burning pain. If he ignores this, the ulcer can wreak havoc. It may eat into a blood vessel and start a hemorrhage; it may gnaw away at the protective mucus and right through the wall of the stomach; or it may completely block the digestive process by obstructing the GI tract.

Peptic ulcers are extremely common; they afflict some 10 to 15 per cent of the population. Much mystery still surrounds them. No one knows, for example, why they occur more frequently in the duodenum than in the stomach, or why more men suffer from them than women do.

Scientists are studying the relationship between hormones and ulcers with antihistamine tests. And laboratories synthesizing highly concentrated prostaglandins, acid inhibitors naturally produced in lesser potency in the body, are testing their products on ulcer patients in hopes that the more powerful man-made substances will effectively suppress excessive secretion of acids in the stomach. Recent research has shown that some ulcers result from a malfunction of the pituitary and adrenal glands. But these malfunctions may themselves be induced by the action of the nervous system. The enormous role played by the nervous system is demonstrated by the fact, familiar to all doctors, that the personal relationship between physician and patient is as important as any other part of the treatment of an ulcer. The ulcer patient seems to benefit as much from the doctor's interest as from any medication he might receive.

Emotional states do not, of course, cause ulcers only, or afflict only the digestive system. Their influence is evident in a host of ailments which range all the way from relatively minor skin irritations like hives and eczema to a fatal heart attack. Still, the digestive system appears to be at least as vulnerable as other parts of the body to emotional disturbances, both major and minor, and in this system the symptoms are more dramatic. One explanation may lie in the bulk, complexity, and copious nerve supply of the GI tract. Obviously, more things can go wrong with an intricate machine than with a simple one.

But when one considers the fantastic complexity of the digestive system, one of the most striking facts about it is that it normally operates for 24 hours a day with great efficiency. Nature, indeed, has been particularly generous in her arrangements for the ingestion and digestion of food. She has not only equipped man's body with a system that requires little assistance from his conscious mind, but has also blessed him with one of the most gratifying and universal of pleasures: that of satisfying his hunger with a hearty meal.

The Digestive Process, Step by Step

In the outline figure of the human head and torso opposite, the body's digestive system is represented as a twisted and convoluted tube. If its turns, coils and folds were straightened out, this tube would average 30 feet (9 m) long in the adult. Within its length takes place an involved chemical conversion every time a gourmet meal or a bedtime snack is eaten. Here, the chemically complex foods man eats are broken down, modified and transmuted into the chemically simple substances his body must have to continue its healthy existence. But none of this involved apparatus can work without the brain and its appetite control center, the appestat, which triggers hunger pangs after measuring the level of nutrients stored in the body or by recalling to mind a memorable meal. Sometimes, just the remembered smell of morning coffee is enough to start the salivary glands working. The intricate steps of digestion are explained as a simplified board game.

A RESTRICTED VARIETY

While food comes in endless variety, the digestive system reduces it to the basic nutrients the body needs for fuel and building. Carbohydrates (as supplied by vegetables, fruit and bread, *(opposite)* and fats (available in ice cream and meat) are converted into simple energy sources. Proteins (from meat and fish) are converted into amino acids, which are the basic building material of the body.

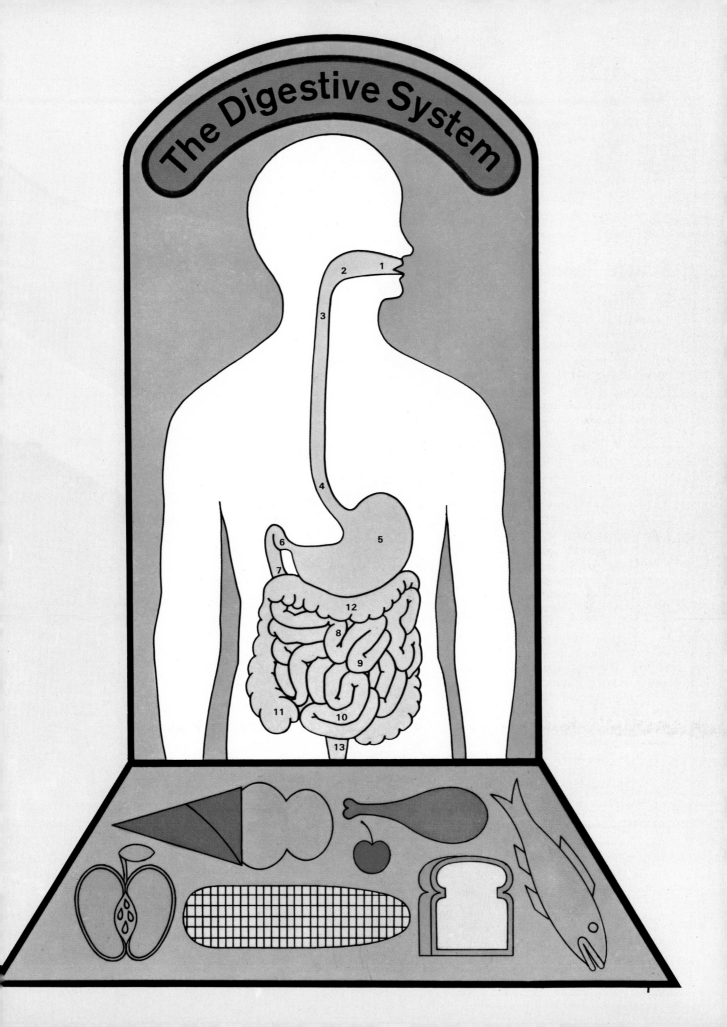

Simple Rules
to Follow

In the game of digestion at right, the players are particles of food and the board is the body. If the game were patentable, it would earn a fortune. It is fun to play—even for the board; it is healthful (if not overindulged); and it is inexpensive (if played with discretion). And it is simple to play because it is almost automated.

The mere contact of food with tissue in the mouth sends a message to the brain, which instantly orders certain glands to deliver saliva. As the teeth grind the food, the saliva lubricates it to facilitate its looping ride through the rest of the system, and also to start digesting carbohydrates.

As the teeth finish their job and the tongue helps the food along its way, care must be taken in crossing the windpipe (2). A trapdoor (the epiglottis) slams shut, forcing the food to take the indicated passageway to the next stage of the journey.

The throat connects to the esophagus, a tube leading to the stomach. By now the food has been chopped up as finely as a purée, but still needs help in moving along. So, the nerve ends of the esophagus order constrictive waves sent down the tube, forcing the food toward the stomach. This wave action is called peristalsis. In the meantime, the stomach *(following pages)* has been alerted and is already releasing gastric juices, preparing for the next move in the game.

The Digestive System

Pay here for saliva and some gastric juices. Proceed immediately to 2.

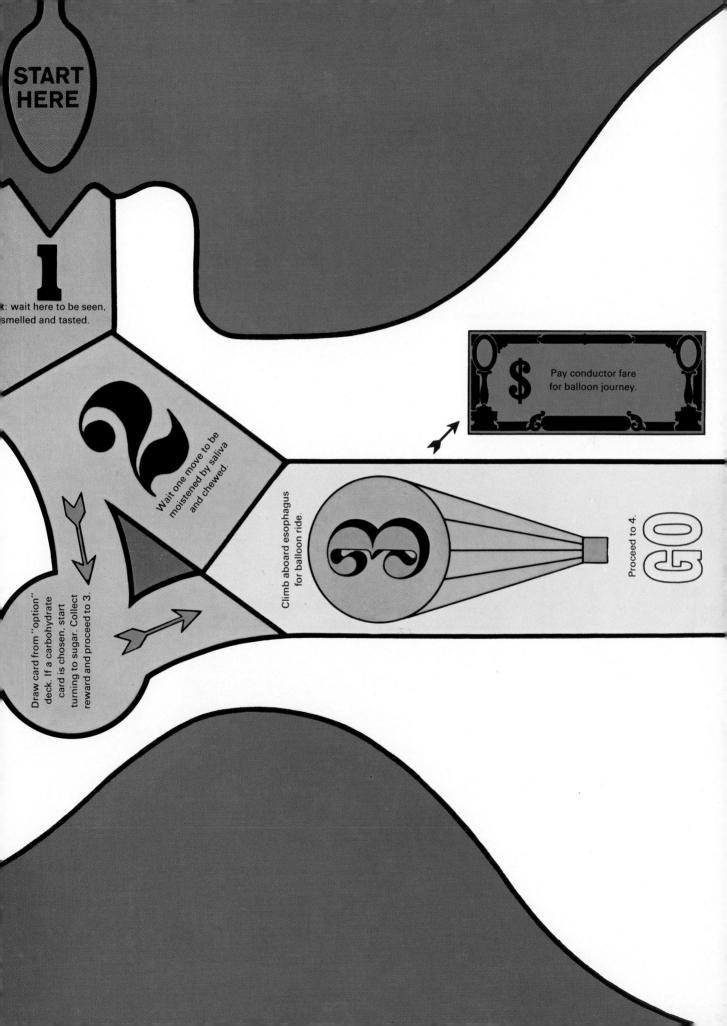

START HERE

1

...t: wait here to be seen, ...smelled and tasted.

2 Wait one move to be moistened by saliva and chewed.

Draw card from "option" deck. If a carbohydrate card is chosen, start turning to sugar. Collect reward and proceed to 3.

3 Climb aboard esophagus for balloon ride.

$ Pay conductor fare for balloon journey.

Proceed to 4. **GO**

The Digestive System

Needed: A Fine Sense of Control

In the game of digestion, every player's cards are stacked and every move is precisely controlled. In the stomach (4), hydrochloric acid and the enzyme pepsin begin to break down the protein, forming simpler materials which will soon become amino acids.

On their own, the acid and the enzyme are strong enough to eat into the wall of the stomach, which is what seems to cause ulcers. Normally, the protective mucus serves as a buffer in the stomach, but increased acid—brought on, for instance, by stress—can eat through this protective stomach lining and break down its resistant quality.

The next move, to the intestines, depends upon the players' readiness (carbohydrates advance more rapidly than proteins; fats are the slowest).

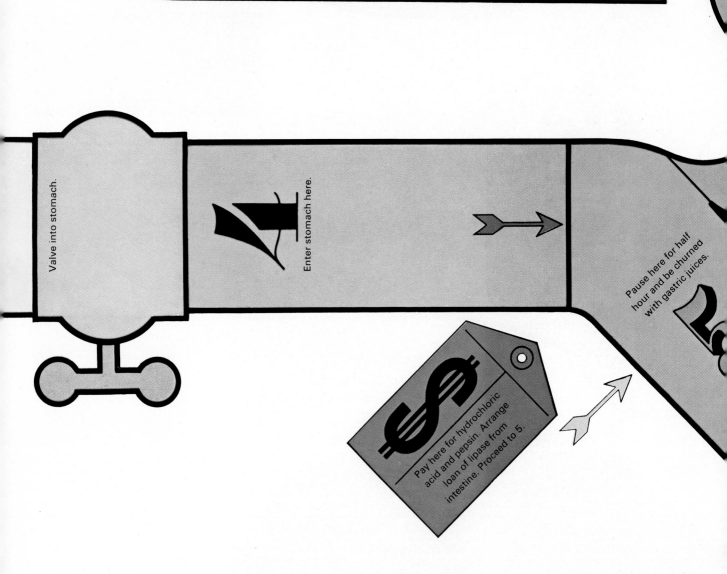

Valve into stomach.

Enter stomach here.

Pause here for half hour and be churned with gastric juices.

Pay here for hydrochloric acid and pepsin. Arrange loan of lipase from intestine. Proceed to 5.

A. Proteins pause here to be broken down by acid and pepsin; collect reward and proceed to 6.

B. Milk proteins pause here to be curdled; wait out one move, then proceed to 6.

C. Small fat particles must pause, use lipase to turn into fatty acids and glycerol. Proceed to 6.

6 INSPECTION

Alcohol wins; take free ride through body; all others pay alcohol's fare.

Partially digested food must purchase passage here for trip to duodenum. Proceed to 7.

ADMIT ONE
FREE RIDE
ALCOHOL

FIRST CLASS PASSAGE
ADMIT ONE

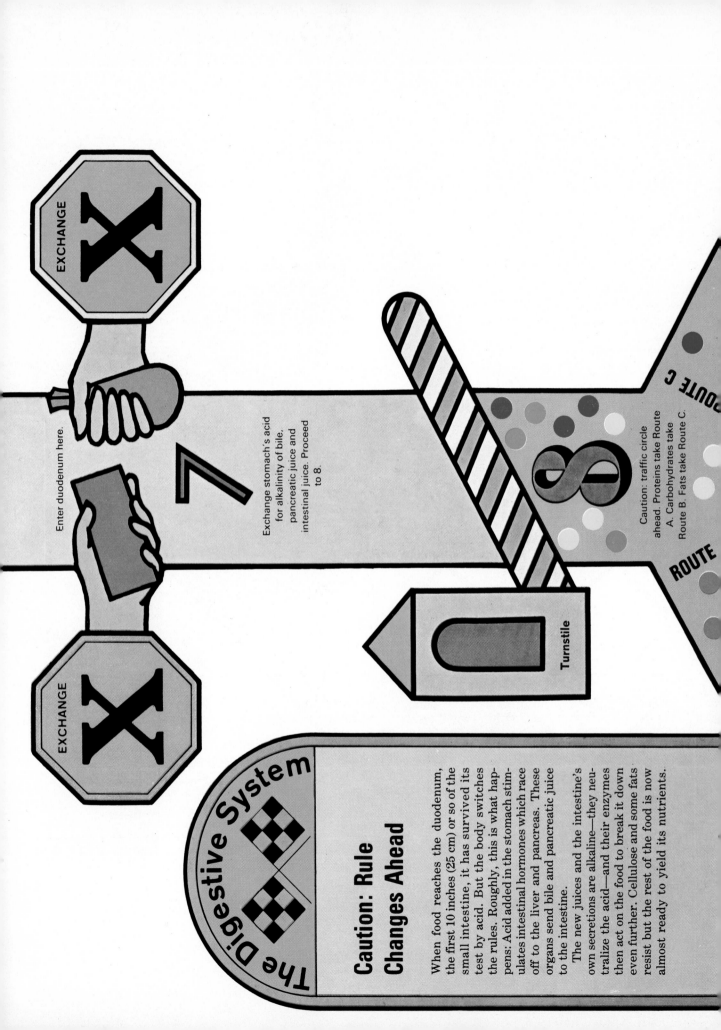

EXCHANGE

EXCHANGE

Enter duodenum here.

7

Exchange stomach's acid for alkalinity of bile, pancreatic juice and intestinal juice. Proceed to 8.

8

Caution: traffic circle ahead. Proteins take Route A. Carbohydrates take Route B. Fats take Route C.

ROUTE C

ROUTE

Turnstile

The Digestive System

Caution: Rule Changes Ahead

When food reaches the duodenum, the first 10 inches (25 cm) or so of the small intestine, it has survived its test by acid. But the body switches the rules. Roughly, this is what happens: Acid added in the stomach stimulates intestinal hormones which race off to the liver and pancreas. These organs send bile and pancreatic juice to the intestine.

The new juices and the intestine's own secretions are alkaline—they neutralize the acid—and their enzymes then act on the food to break it down even further. Cellulose and some fats resist but the rest of the food is now almost ready to yield its nutrients.

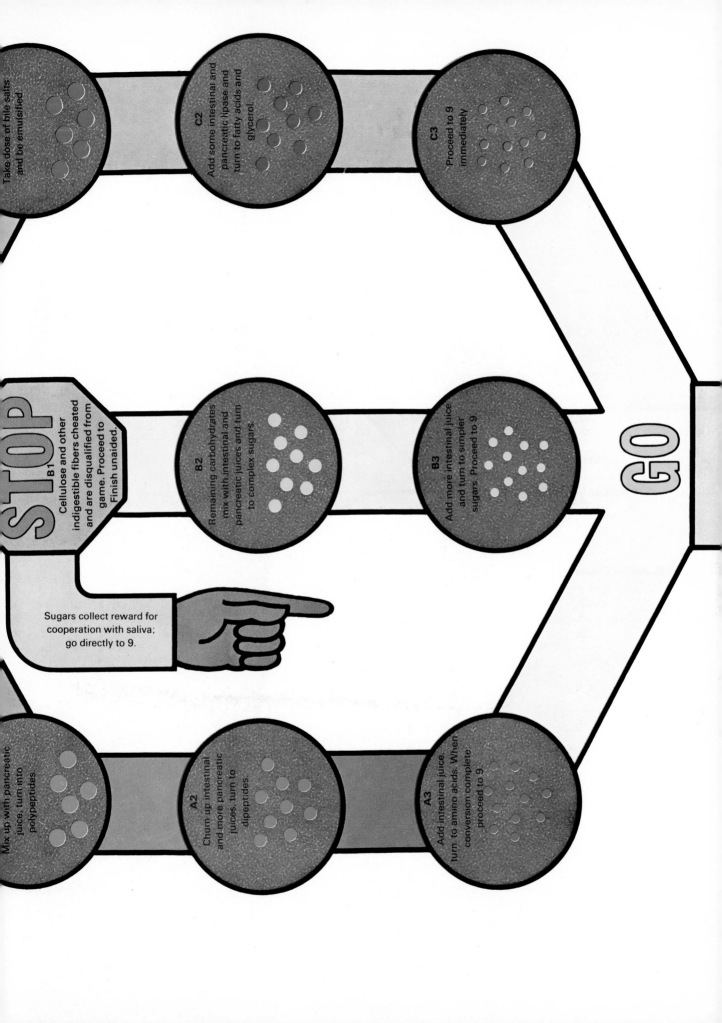

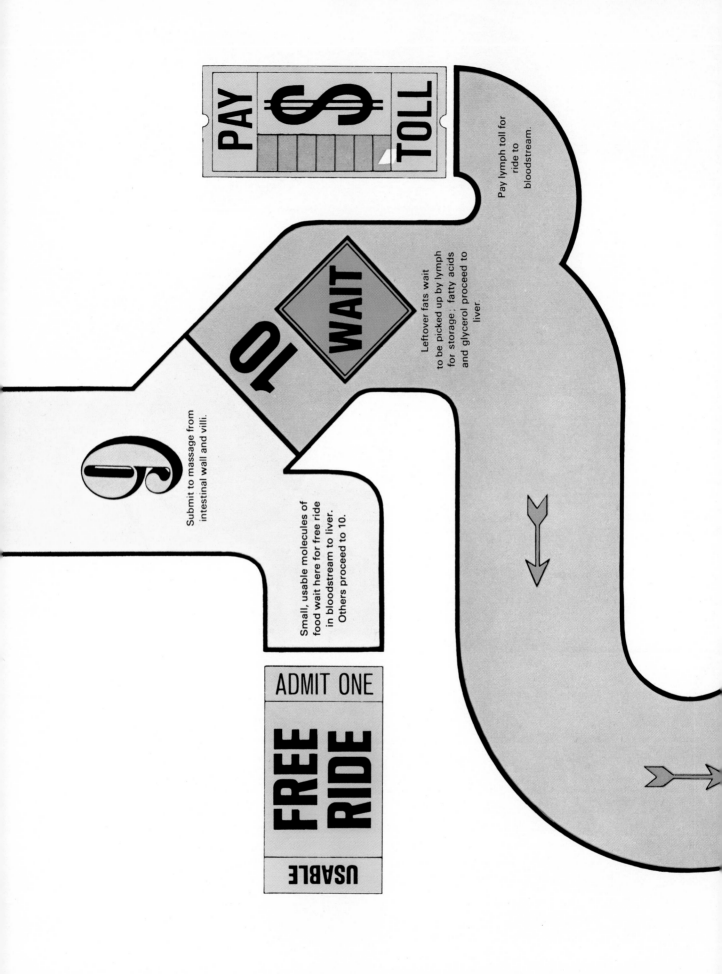

PAY $ TOLL

Pay lymph toll for ride to bloodstream.

WAIT

10

Leftover fats wait to be picked up by lymph for storage: fatty acids and glycerol proceed to liver.

Submit to massage from intestinal wall and villi.

9

Small, usable molecules of food wait here for free ride in bloodstream to liver. Others proceed to 10.

ADMIT ONE

FREE RIDE

USABLE

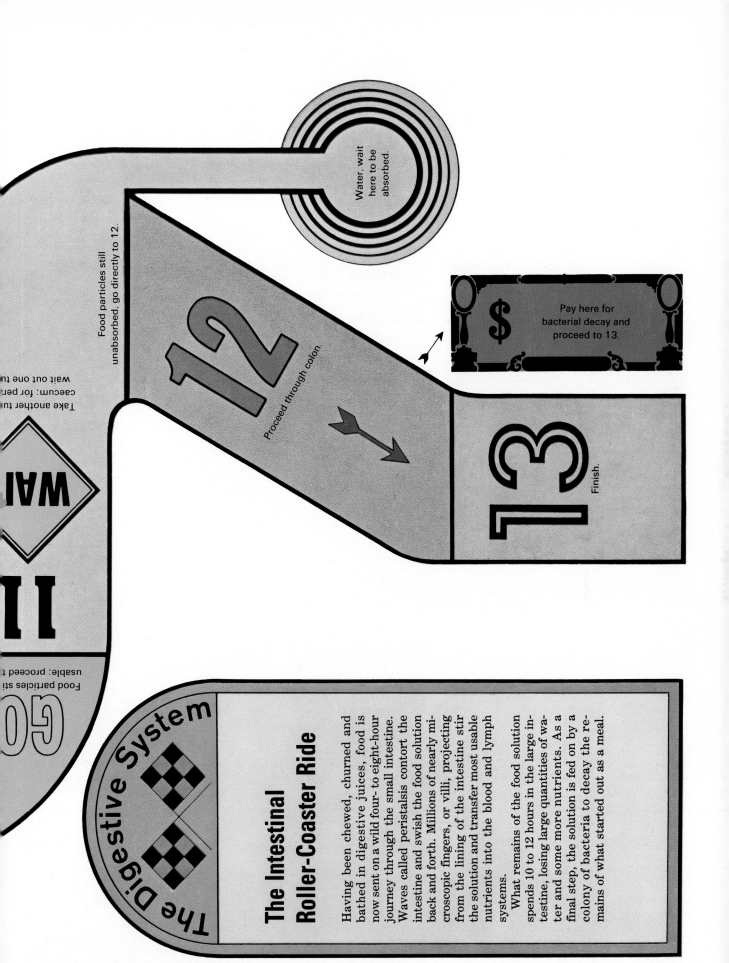

The Digestive System

The Intestinal Roller-Coaster Ride

Having been chewed, churned and bathed in digestive juices, food is now sent on a wild four- to eight-hour journey through the small intestine. Waves called peristalsis contort the intestine and swish the food solution back and forth. Millions of nearly microscopic fingers, or villi, projecting from the lining of the intestine stir the solution and transfer most usable nutrients into the blood and lymph systems.

What remains of the food solution spends 10 to 12 hours in the large intestine, losing large quantities of water and some more nutrients. As a final step, the solution is fed on by a colony of bacteria to decay the remains of what started out as a meal.

Water, wait here to be absorbed.

Food particles still unabsorbed, go directly to 12.

12 Proceed through colon.

Pay here for bacterial decay and proceed to 13.

13 Finish.

Take another tu... caecum; for per... wait out one tu...

Food particles sti... usable; proceed t...

GO

WAI...

6

The Vital Pairs:
The Lungs
and Kidneys

WHEN JOHN DONNE WROTE THAT "No man is an island, entire of itself," he was referring to the mind and the spirit of man. His classic phrase, however, can be applied to the body of man as well. For no human body can flourish independent of the world beyond its own skin. Like a medieval castle, it has its fortifications and protective moats. Yet it is far from self-sustaining. From the surrounding environment it must obtain food, water and oxygen; it must send back out the wastes which would otherwise poison it. To ensure this essential passage both ways, it must have its means of entry and exit.

The body has three main gateways: the digestive tract, discussed in the previous chapter; the lungs, through which we take in oxygen and breathe out carbon dioxide; and the kidneys, through which we excrete wastes in the form of urine. Unlike the drawbridges of the medieval castle, these gateways do not stand at the body's outermost ramparts; nevertheless, they mark the boundaries between its inside and outside. This seeming paradox has its roots in a popular misconception. To the layman, a cinder in the eye, a splinter embedded under the nail, the morsel of food just popped into the mouth, are all unarguably "inside" the body. To the physiologist, however, they are really only on its outskirts. The scientist considers food to be inside the body only after it has been digested and absorbed through the intestinal lining; oxygen only after it has been absorbed through the lung membrane. Water and waste materials are considered to be outside the body immediately after they have been filtered out of the kidneys into the bladder.

Among the wonders of construction with which the body has been endowed, both the lungs and kidneys rank high on the list. As if in token of the crucial nature of their allotted tasks, each is a paired organ. Many a human being is alive and thriving today, despite damage or actual removal of one lung or kidney, because the remaining organ fills the breach and continues to do the work of both.

This is but one indication, however, of the importance to the body of the proper functioning of its respiratory and excretory systems. The body's trillions of cells require so much oxygen that we need about 30 times as much surface for its intake as our entire skin area covers. The lungs provide this surface area—even though they weigh only about two and a half pounds, and fit neatly within the chest cavity—by virtue of the fact that their membranes fold over and over on themselves in pockets so thin that a sheet of the finest paper seems grossly thick by comparison. The kidneys, each of which is no more than four or five inches long, are no less astonishingly equipped for their particular duties. An estimated 42 gallons (159 l) of water—about three times the body's entire weight in fluid—filter down the kidney tubules every day. This flood is dealt with by millions of tiny mechanisms called nephrons,

THE BREATH OF LIFE
The functioning of the lungs is most readily apparent in winter, when the cold quickly condenses moisture-laden puffs of exhaled air into miniature clouds. In their crucial capacity as a medium of exchange, the lungs sustain life by unloading carbon dioxide and taking in oxygen. Carried by the blood to the cells, oxygen unlocks the energy contained in the body's fuels.

working in shifts and selectively reabsorbing most of the fluid back into the bloodstream.

Selectivity, indeed, is the key to the activities of both kidneys and lungs. It is brought into play from the very instant that we take a breath of air. This holds true whether we are inhaling the stagnant air of a crowded cocktail party or the salt sea breeze on a lonely beach, for despite the forebodings of fresh-air fiends, the lungs handle both kinds with equal efficiency.

Even the purest country air contains dust particles and bacteria; city air, of course, also has soot and exhaust fumes. Whatever its content, the air, in the few seconds it takes to travel from the environment to the lungs, must pass inspection by a preliminary board of review: the nose; the trachea, or windpipe; the bronchi—two large tubes, one for each lung—into which the windpipe divides behind the breastbone; and finally, issuing from the main bronchi, the smaller bronchi and tiny bronchioles—much like branches and twigs stemming from a tree trunk.

As it moves into these channels, the air attracts vigilant attention. In the nose, some of its dust particles and bacteria drop off simply because they cannot make their way through the twisting nasal passages; others are trapped by mucus or by tiny hairs, cilia, that beat in a direction opposite to the incoming air flow. In the windpipe, most of the remaining bacteria in the air are intercepted by mucus; so are particles that have gotten past the nose. When sufficiently irritating, the impurities accumulated in the nose and the particles in the windpipe respectively produce the explosive irritations we know as the sneeze and the cough.

Two studies in pink

Once beyond the nose and windpipe, the incoming air has received most of the screening it is going to get. The bronchi and bronchioles serve primarily as conduits direct to the lungs. The air they finally bring to the lungs has been cleansed as much as the valiant efforts of the preliminary channels—and the nature of the particular breather's environment—will permit. How heavily environmental factors figure may be seen in the contrast between an infant's lungs and those of an adult city-dweller with the smoking habit. The infant's lungs are a bright, healthy pink; the adult's, a dull pink-and-gray, mottled with black.

Arriving at the bronchioles, the air has yet to unload its cargo of oxygen. The start of this task is taken on by vast armies of tiny, expansible, thin-walled, clustering sacs called alveoli, in which the bronchioles terminate. The alveoli constitute the bulk of lung tissue; it is their substance which makes the lungs soft and spongy, and indeed so light that they can float. The lungs of an average-sized man contain an estimated 300 to 400 million of these air sacs. When the chest expands or contracts—on stimulus from a respiratory center in the brain—it is in fact the alveoli that are expanding or contracting. Their expansion provides the vital surface required for oxygen intake into the blood; the enormous area covered by the membrane of the alveolar cells, in total, is some 280 square feet (27 m^2).

A fateful film of moisture

The membrane of the alveoli is moist—another crucial factor. Oxygen, in its original gaseous state, cannot diffuse in the bloodstream; it must first be dissolved. The film of moisture coating the alveolar membrane effects this transformation. The evolution of this delicate apparatus deep within the body of man was, indeed, responsible for his ability to live exclusively on land. Amphibian animals, such as frogs, breathe directly through their skins as well as through their lungs. Had human animals not developed a breathing membrane that stayed moist of itself, they might have had to face the somewhat impractical prospect of keeping their skin permanently wet in order to breathe at all.

Still another superlative bit of engineering helps effect the final entry of oxygen into the bloodstream. Into each lung a pulmonary artery carries a surge of blood directly from the heart, seeking fresh oxygen. In the lung, each of these arteries divides and subdivides into smaller and smaller vessels, dogging the paths of the small bronchi and bronchioles. Where the tiniest bronchioles terminate in the clusters of alveoli, the pulmonary vessels open out into a rich network of capillaries which surround each cluster like faithful shadows. Layers of capillary and alveolar cells thus lie in direct contact side by side—a double membrane, almost unimaginably thin, with air moving on one side and blood flowing past on the other.

Diffused into the blood via this virtually transparent wall, the oxygen molecules are snatched up by the hemoglobin in the blood. They cannot escape back into the lungs; as mentioned in Chapter 4, the iron in the hemoglobin locks the oxygen in a chemical embrace. Swept along in the bloodstream, the oxygen finally arrives at the body's waiting cells, there to unite with the body's fuels and free the energy in them.

The actual quantity of oxygen taken in during this process may vary from one minute to another, depending on the rate of breathing and the speed with which blood is being pumped through the arteries. This, in turn, depends on how much energy the body requires at the time. A man snoozing in a hammock may absorb only half a pint of oxygen a minute. A miler trying to beat a world's record may soak up more than five quarts in the same period.

The lungs do not rest on their laurels with the delivery of oxygen to the bloodstream. Simultaneously, they remove the waste carbon dioxide

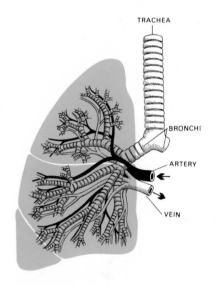

A CLOSE LOOK AT A LUNG
Air pulled down the trachea into the bronchi and lungs enters a network of millions of moist air sacs capable of expanding and contracting. Blood enters the lung via an artery and flows around the sacs in capillaries, giving up carbon dioxide and taking on oxygen. It then flows through a vein to the heart. The right lung, shown here, has three lobes: the smaller left lung has only two, making room for the heart.

which results from the combustion of carbon compounds in the cells. Picked up from these cells and carried along by the blood on its way to pick up oxygen from the lungs, the carbon dioxide is brought alongside the alveolar membrane, and passes out from the bloodstream just as the oxygen passes in. Although the two gases pass through the same membrane, they have little to do with each other. They are like total strangers boarding and leaving a train at a single signal. From the lungs, the carbon dioxide makes its way out of the body along the same route which the oxygen followed on its way in.

While an excess of carbon dioxide would be poisonous to the body, its complete removal would be fatal. A small amount is retained in the blood, and that amount is vital to life, as one of the great regulators of the chemistry of the body. It not only maintains the proper degree of acidity in body fluid but also controls the internal breathing mechanism.

A case of Jekyll and Hyde

The Jekyll-Hyde nature of carbon dioxide was confirmed only in recent decades. Its existence in the air was discovered as far back as the 17th Century by the Belgian scientist, Johann Baptista van Helmont. Its presence in the body, as a by-product of respiration, was discovered a century later by a Scottish chemist, Joseph Black. Not surprisingly, Black assumed that carbon dioxide was simply a waste. Then, in 1885, a German physiologist, Johann Friedrich Miescher-Rüsch, suggested that carbon dioxide actually played a major role in regulating how hard and fast we breathe. Twenty years later, two British physiologists, John Scott Haldane and an associate, J. G. Priestley, confirmed this assumption.

Haldane was one of those colorful individualists whose nonconformist behavior adds spice to the sedate annals of scientific research. One of his habits was to carry a watch which lacked a minute hand, ticking only the hours away; nevertheless he used it to keep appointments and was said never to have missed a train. He also indulged in the far greater gamble of experimenting on himself. When he began his investigations of the breathing process, it was common knowledge that people who become excited and breathe too quickly often suffer numbness, and sometimes even an uncontrollable twitching. These unpleasant sensations had generally been attributed to "oxygen poisoning," but Haldane thought they were more likely to be caused by the exhalation of too much carbon dioxide.

According to a popular medical school legend, one of the ways Haldane tested his theory was to sit on a stool in a steaming shower and pant furiously for several minutes. Soon he began to feel the expected symptoms. But by the time he was sure his theory was right—the story goes—his muscles were cramping so uncontrollably that he could nei-

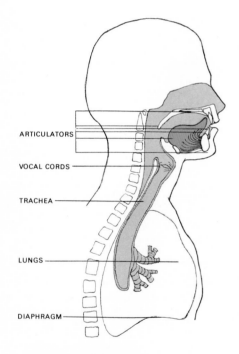

THE THEATER OF SOUND
Speech is produced by many muscular movements employing all of the body's orchestral parts, shown above. A sound begins when the lungs drive a current of air upward through the trachea and set the vocal cords vibrating in the larynx. The sound is now shaped in the air passage *(gray)* by movements of the articulators *(right)*—teeth, palate, lips, jaws and tongue—into the various vowel and consonant sounds of speech.

ARTICULATORS

VOCAL CORDS

TRACHEA

LUNGS

DIAPHRAGM

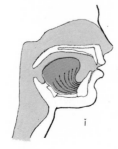

ī

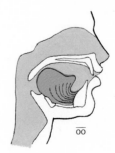

 ̄oo

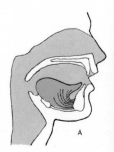

A

ther turn off the shower nor get out of the shower room. Luckily an assistant happened by to rescue him.

Haldane always denied this story. In any case, in other experiments in closed respiration chambers, and under varying conditions of atmospheric pressure, he and Priestley demonstrated that carbon dioxide regulates the breathing through its effect on the respiratory center in the brain. To a certain very limited extent, we ourselves can decide to breathe lightly or deeply, slowly or quickly; in this sense we can control our respiration. But when such decisions bring the breather close to the danger point, the involuntary-control system takes over. After a few minutes of holding his breath, for example, a person is forced to inhale quickly and deeply. He does so, Haldane and Priestley proved, because carbon dioxide accumulates in his blood and stimulates the respiratory center to dictate renewed breathing.

Under normal conditions, the respiratory system works so smoothly that we are not even aware of it. It can, however, be interfered with in a number of ways: by the diversion of a piece of food into the windpipe, by certain ailments and by the inhalation of certain chemical fumes.

The illnesses which can affect the respiratory system are considerable in number. The common cold obstructs breathing by causing watery mucus to collect in the nose and block the flow of incoming air. The even more troublesome inflammation known as bronchitis obstructs the air flow by causing the lining of the air tubes to swell and to secrete large amounts of sticky mucus. Asthma, often brought on by allergy, anxiety or tension, can make muscles in the bronchi contract so that the victim wheezes and gasps for air. And with emphysema, in which some of the alveoli degenerate and others become expanded, the lungs' elasticity is diminished and the area available for respiration decreases. Smoking, allergies, and industrial and urban pollutants are prime contributors to these chronic pulmonary diseases. The worst damage to the lungs occurs when the alveoli are injured so that oxygen cannot pass through them into the bloodstream. Such damage can be wrought by tuberculosis, which can destroy lung tissue, or by pneumonia, the lung inflammation which fills the alveoli with a sticky substance that keeps air from penetrating the membrane leading to the blood. This pair of diseases—the two worst killers in the United States in 1900—has been checked by the development of antibiotic drugs, but both are still dangerous.

Finality in a capsule

In addition to the obstruction of the air pipes and damage to the lung membrane, another means by which the body can be robbed of oxygen is through the intake of certain poisons. Hermann Goering, the second-ranking man in the Nazi hierarchy, cheated the executioner after the

Nuremberg war-crimes trials in 1946 by swallowing a capsule of potassium cyanide, a chemical which prevents the proper use of oxygen by the cells. Another killer is carbon monoxide, inhaled from a defective stove or automobile exhaust pipe. Carbon monoxide, unlike carbon dioxide, has no redeeming features whatever. It cannot be usefully employed by the body. But by a fluke of nature, it attaches itself even more readily than oxygen to the hemoglobin in the blood. By doing so, it displaces the oxygen, much as a cowbird hatched in another bird's nest will hog so much of the food that the legitimate nestlings starve.

Whatever its cause, anoxia—the cutting off of oxygen from the cells—will result in quick death. As Haldane himself expressed it, it not only brings about "the stoppage of a machine, it is also the total ruin of the supposed machinery."

The traffic passing through the gateway of the lungs is no more critical, however, than the traffic passing through the gateway of the kidneys. Besides carbon dioxide, the cells of the body cast off a host of unwanted substances, including nitrogen compounds, sulphates and phosphates. These remnants may be compared to the ashes left after a fire has burned all the coal it can. They, too, must be removed if the cellular furnaces are to function effectively, and their removal is the task of the kidneys.

These dark red organs, which have a characteristic bean shape, are situated near the spine, in the middle of the back, just behind the stomach and the liver. The kidneys are, except for the brain, perhaps the most complex organs in the body. Ridding the body of wastes is only one of their jobs. They also regulate the chemical makeup of the blood and preserve the correct balance between salt and water in the body.

A miracle of ingenuity

The method by which the kidneys clean the wastes out of the bloodstream, where the cells have dumped them, is a miracle of ingenuity. When the blood flows into the kidneys, it is immediately channeled into clusters of capillaries. Each cluster, so small that the eye can barely see it, is called a glomerulus, from the Latin for "small ball." It is tightly enclosed by a double membrane which leads into a tubule, or little tube. The glomerulus, the membrane and the tubule together make up a single, highly intricate mechanism called a nephron. There are about two and a half million nephrons and, if all their tubules were straightened out, they would stretch for approximately 50 miles (80 km).

The kidneys do not simply pick waste products out of the bloodstream and send them along for final disposal. As blood courses through the glomeruli, much of its fluid, containing both useful chemicals and dissolved waste materials, filters out through the membranes, much as carbon dioxide filters into the lungs. Once through the membranes, it

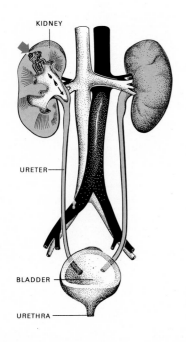

KIDNEY

URETER

BLADDER

URETHRA

CLEANSERS OF THE BODY'S FLUIDS
The two kidneys, with their ability to excrete unwanted materials and retain others, are the body's chief organs for cleansing its internal fluids. The kidneys are equipped with filtering, absorbing and secreting units called nephrons, shown much enlarged (arrow) at left and in detail opposite. Ureters carry the resulting urine to the bladder for temporary storage. Finally, the urine is discharged through the urethra.

flows on into the tubules. The tubules proceed to send back into the bloodstream what is valuable and re-usable, leaving the waste products neatly trapped outside. This recapture of needed materials is carried out by chemical action. As the tubules twist and wind away from the glomeruli, they come back into contact with other capillaries. Here the valuable sugars and salt which have filtered into the tubules are seized by enzymes and yanked back into the bloodstream. At the same time, molecules of water are being forced back under pressure. The body cannot afford to lose the estimated 42 gallons (159 l) of water that daily soak into the tubules in order to dissolve the departing wastes; therefore, most of it must be drawn back. Altogether, about 99 per cent of the fluid which filters out of the glomeruli is reabsorbed into the bloodstream. As it flows on down the tubules, the remaining 1 per cent, along with the wastes, is converted into urine. This drops into two other channels—the ureters—and then into the bladder to await expulsion.

The telltale trail of sugar

Even when the kidneys are operating at peak efficiency, the nephrons can reabsorb only so much sugar and water. Their limitations are dramatically illustrated in cases of *diabetes mellitus*, a disease which causes the amount of sugar in the blood to rise far above normal. Ordinarily, all the glucose that seeps out through the glomeruli into the tubules is reabsorbed into the blood. But if too much is present, the tubules reach the limit of their ability to pass the sugar back into the bloodstream, and retain some of it. It is then carried along in the urine, often providing a doctor with his first clue that a patient has *diabetes mellitus*. Indeed, the value of urine as a diagnostic aid has been known to the world of medicine as far back as the time of Hippocrates. From then on, examination of the urine became a regular procedure for physicians, and by the Middle Ages its study achieved the status of a science, uroscopy.

Because of the abiding importance of both the kidneys and the lungs to the maintenance of life, great effort has been expended to find substitute devices that can take over when either of these organs even partially fails beyond repair. One of the most notable successes along this line has been the kidney machine, a device that can be attached to an artery and vein several times a week so that wastes can be filtered from the patient's bloodstream. Several different types have been developed, including some that can be used at home, and others that are portable. In 1978, the lives of over 72,000 persons worldwide were being sustained through the use of artificial kidneys, known as dialysis; most of these patients were being treated at home or in clinics.

Both lungs and kidneys have garnered a large share of attention in the increasingly widespread effort to effect transplantations of internal or-

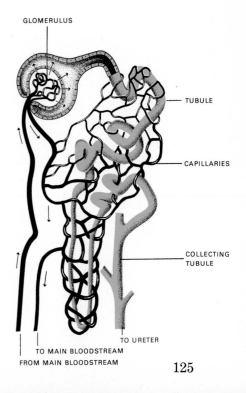

THE WORK OF THE NEPHRONS
The process of forming urine begins when arterial blood flows into a tuft of capillaries (the glomerulus) in the nephron, which filters out some of its fluid—not all of it waste. The fluid enters the tubule of the nephron, where useful sugars, salts and water are reabsorbed by capillaries and returned to the main bloodstream. The capillaries in turn secrete ammonia through the tubule wall into the fluid. The resulting waste is urine.

GLOMERULUS

TUBULE

CAPILLARIES

COLLECTING TUBULE

TO URETER

TO MAIN BLOODSTREAM

FROM MAIN BLOODSTREAM

gans. Thus far the kidney has proved the easiest of all organs to transplant, primarily because the surgical connection involved is the easiest. Since 1954, more than 40,000 kidney transplants have been performed in many parts of the world. The most successful of these have involved transplants between twins, whose blood and tissues are most closely matched, but even grafts from donors unrelated to the patients have extended the lives of a great many people.

New research offers still brighter hopes of overcoming the basic problem in transplantation, that of finding ways to override the body's natural tendency to reject strange intrusions. It is now believed, for example, that body cells, like blood cells, exist in distinctive types. Tests can show whether patient and donor have similar cell types; if they do, the transplant is much more likely to take. This procedure does not completely avoid rejection, however, and drugs must be employed to forestall it. These drugs have proved to be very effective, but they must be administered for long periods of time, and they have the serious disadvantage of disabling the body's defense against infection. As a consequence, some patients have succumbed to the ordinary bacteria present in all human bodies. But even such obstacles, it is believed, will be overcome in time. On this score, as on all the other life or death matters with which they deal, medical scientists remain incurable optimists.

Replacements for the Body's Faulty Parts

Ever since Hindu surgeons, about 800 B.C., used flaps of forehead skin to repair an amputated nose, doctors have dreamed of replacing damaged organs with tissue from a healthy donor. Every imaginable kind of transplantation has been tried, on animals *(opposite)* and on humans. Yet, with rare exceptions, tissue transplanted from one human being or species to another is doomed to die. Each individual is genetically unique, right down to his cells and proteins. Thus, when tissue is transplanted, it is regarded by the host as antigenic—that is, as an alien substance. It is rejected by means of the host's anitbody-producing cells, the weapons it also uses against bacteria, which damage the alien cells of the graft. Undaunted, scientists hunt for better ways to make a body accept donated kidneys, lungs and other organs. This search, as well as the development of ingenious mechanical substitutes for organs, is depicted on the following pages.

INCOMPATIBLE RABBITS

The two white rabbits shown opposite, of different breeds, are rejecting skin grafts exchanged between them. The left ear of each bears a patch of skin taken from the other rabbit, and held in place with stitches. The transplanted tissue, which appears dark and scablike in the photograph, dies off because the host's built-in defenses destroy cells that are genetically different from its own.

The Medical Washing Machine

Until transplanted tissue can be used to replace diseased organs, some patients can be kept alive by artificial spare parts. Mechanical kidney substitutes are particularly effective in filtering wastes from the body. When both kidneys fail, either temporarily or permanently, the blood is soon poisoned with nitrogenous wastes, a condition called uremia.

Each year uremia kills about 7,000 persons who might have been saved by either a successful transplant or a machine. About 40,000 people in the United States are now maintained—some temporarily, some permanently—by artificial kidneys, or hemodialysis machines.

Although the machines vary in design, they all work on the same principle. Blood tapped from a vein in the forearm *(right)* is drawn into a compartment inside the machine, where a cellophane membrane allows small molecules of waste to pass by diffusion *(below)* into a cleaning fluid, or dialysate. This membrane can also permit replacement body chemicals to pass from the dialysate into the blood. The clean blood, whose cells are too large to fit through the pores of the membrane, is then filtered to remove any air bubbles and pumped back into the forearm vein.

The treatment is expensive: up to $35,000 a year per patient in special dialysis centers. Efforts are under way, however, to make kidney care better and cheaper. One cost saver has been home dialysis, in which the patient is trained to perform the procedure himself with the help of family members. Also in the planning stage are wearable artificial kidneys, and there is even a device that can make dialysis within the stomach possible.

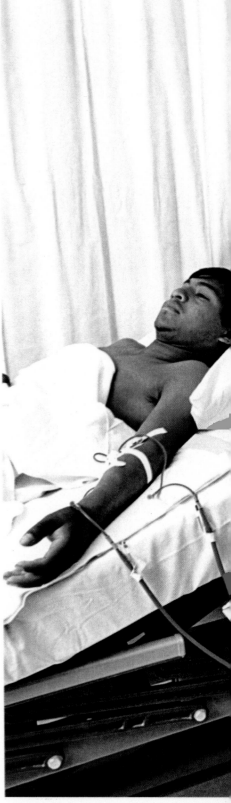

RINSING OUT THE WASTES

The diagram below shows how blood is cleaned and enriched by dialysis. Waste particles *(black)* in the blood and nutrients *(white)* in the dialysate are small enough to diffuse through the semipermeable membrane *(center)*, while the larger blood cells *(red)* cannot. A constant flow of fresh dialysate gradually removes all waste particles and replaces them with nutrients.

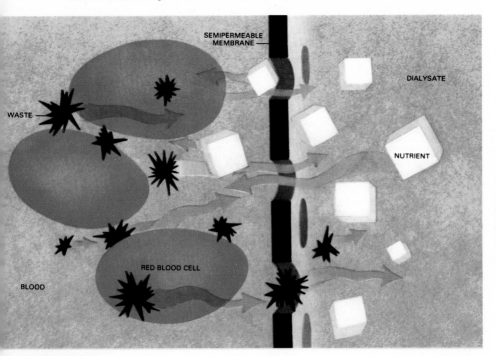

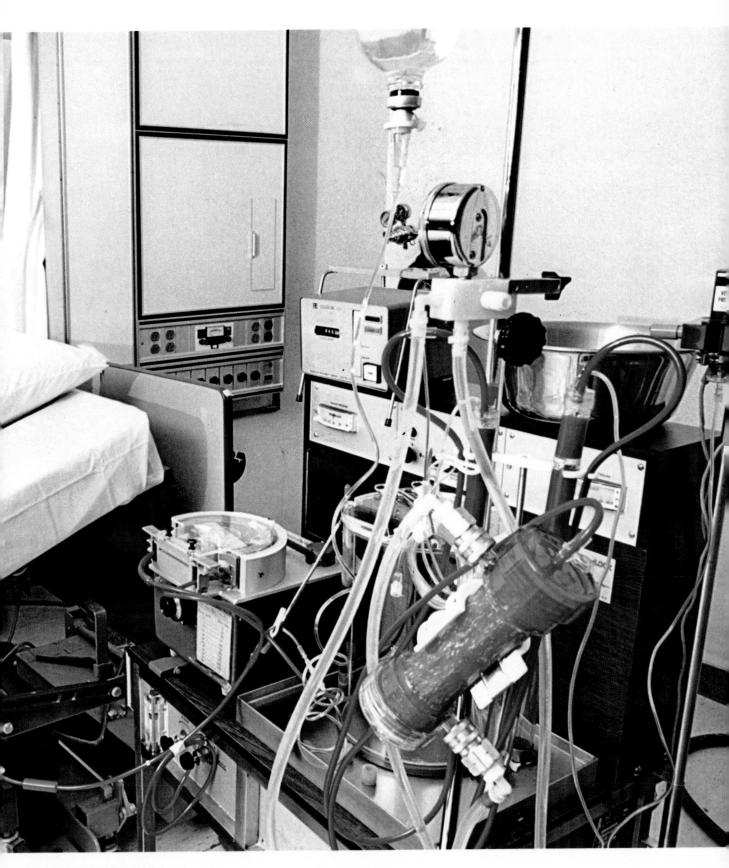

MECHANICAL LEASE ON LIFE
The artificial kidney above removes toxic wastes from a patient's five to six quarts (4.7 to 5.7 l) of blood in about four to five hours, during which time the blood is pumped through the machine twice every hour. Uremic patients must attach themselves to this machine three times a week by means of plastic tubes, inserted in a vein that has been surgically enlarged for easier access.

Stand-ins for Heart and Lungs

One of the most ingenious additions to the modern operating room is the machine at right, which can perform the functions of both the heart and the lungs. Blood is siphoned off from the patient into the machine, bypassing those vital organs but continuing to circulate through the body—permitting surgical procedures on the heart that take up to three hours. Carbon dioxide is removed from the blood and oxygen added—normally done in the lungs—in a bubble chamber. The blood is then defoamed to remove all bubbles—leftover bubbles could be fatal—and piped back into the patient's aorta. A small electric pump provides a "heartbeat."

Since it was developed in the late 1940s, the heart-lung machine has enabled surgeons to perform a variety of delicate procedures, from replacing diseased heart valves to transplanting entire organs.

Bioengineers are now at work developing mechanical hearts and lungs small enough to plant inside the body where they could permanently replace worn-out organs. They are trying to miniaturize a plastic membrane device that could replace a lung, and have placed artificial hearts powered by electromagnets in calves with success. The first such heart might be ready for a human in a few years.

MAKING A LIFE-SAVING DETOUR
During a delicate coronary bypass operation, the technician at right monitors the console of a heart-lung machine. This apparatus pumps blood diverted from the patient's lungs back into his bloodstream. The blood flows through the tubing to the chamber at left foreground, where it is oxygenated, defoamed and filtered before being returned to the patient's body.

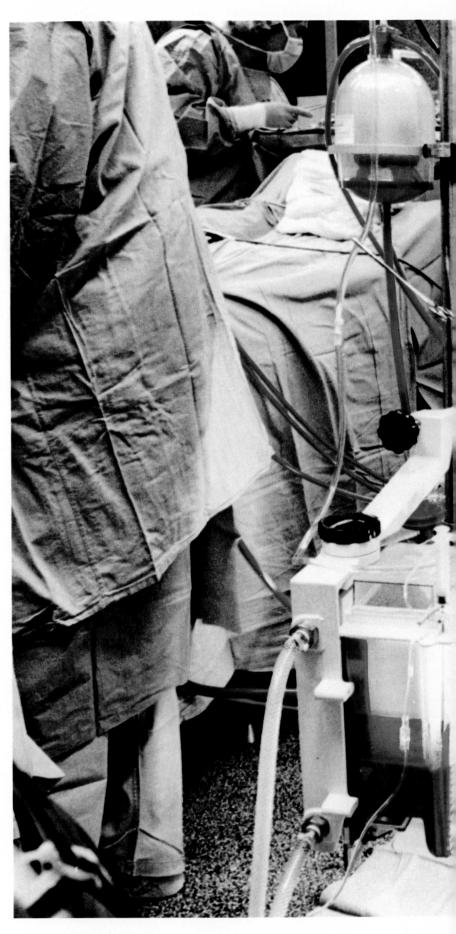

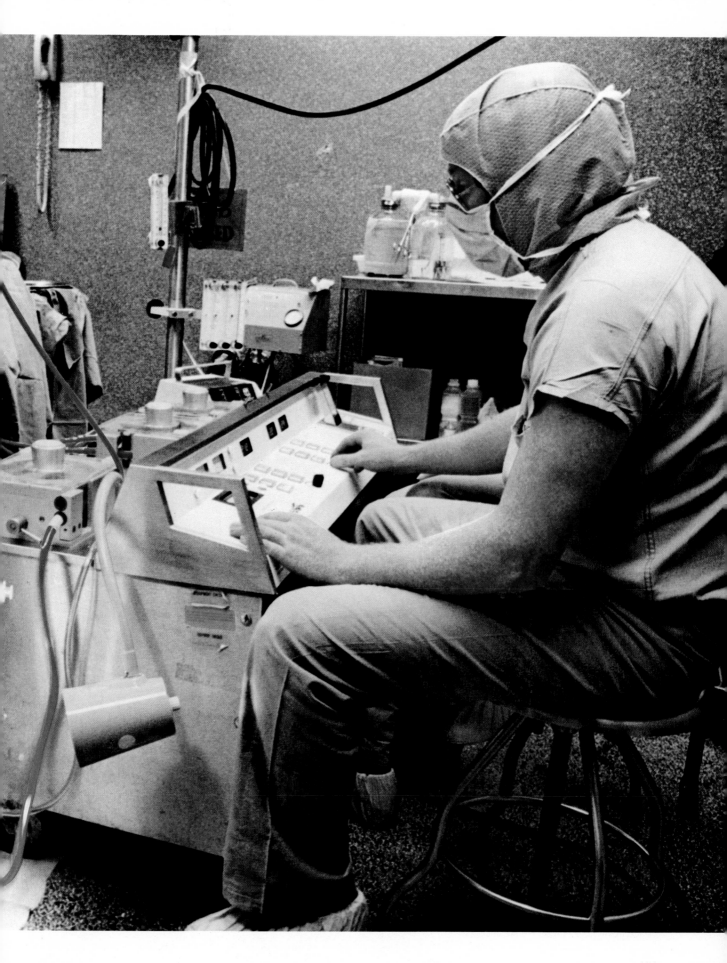

The Mixed Blessing of Immunity

The best machines are only makeshift substitutes for living tissue: Many surgeons prefer transplanting a live organ to implanting an artificial one. This practice, however, always leads to a conflict between the alien tissue and the host's immune system. The protein molecules of the graft's cells become provocative antigens—literally, things that generate antibodies—in their new home. They quickly attract the host's lymphocytes, the immune system's first line of defense. These summon the appropriate anti-

bodies, large, unique proteins which can be tailored to counteract specific antigens *(opposite)*. Some of the lymphocytes are converted into miniature factories which produce vast quantities of specific antibodies.

The immune system attacks the grafted tissue with antibodies and "killer" lymphocytes which invade and eventually destroy the new tissue. Ironically, this mechanism, evolved for disease immunity, will not tolerate a grafted organ which could make the difference between life and death.

To reduce the possibility of rejection, human tissue is typed, or classified—much as blood is—in groups, according to its antigens. The donor's tissue and several possible recipients can be tested and compared for the best match—and the least immune reaction. In one of the most widely used methods, the donor's lymphocytes are tested on the antibodies of potential recipients to determine if there is sufficient compatability to prevent a devastating attack on the cells of the donated tissue *(below)*.

A CLUE TO MATCHMAKING
Blue dye from a special multineedled syringe is injected into a tray whose wells contain mixtures of lymphocytes taken from a potential kidney donor and antibodies from potential recipients. The lymphocytes killed by the antibodies turn blue, which indicates transplant rejection.

FIXING THE ODDS
Peering through a microscope at a tray of exposed lymphocytes, a technician examines each of the wells to determine the ratio of living cells to dead cells. If all of the cells in any one well are living, the chances that the transplant will be successful for that recipient are excellent.

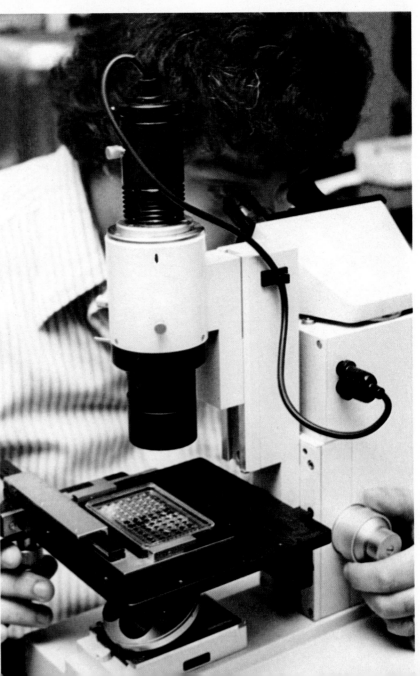

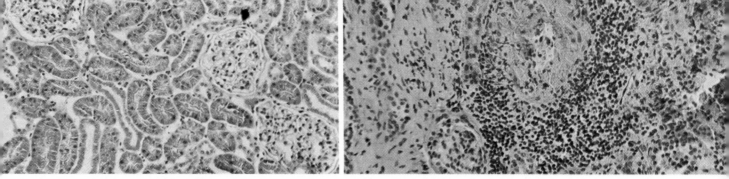

These photomicrographs of transplanted kidney tissue show its transformation from a healthy state *(left)* to a degenerate one.

AN ATTACK ON ALIEN TISSUE

The schematic diagram below illustrates the manner in which the immune system of the body operates to reject the tissue of a transplanted kidney. Antigens *(red)*, which cover the exterior of the transplanted cells *(brown)*, break away from the donor's grafted tissue into the recipient's lymph node at right. Here the antigens stimulate an immune reaction from two types of lymphocyte cells. The so-called B cells *(blue)* are gradually transformed into plasma cells *(gray)* which produce and release specific antibodies *(green)*. The T cells *(purple)* proliferate and become killers which join the antibodies in scurrying from the lymph node to the kidney tissue, searching for alien antigens to attack and setting the rejection process in motion. Assisting in pressing the attack on the damaged and deteriorating tissue cells *(speckled)* are other T and B cells in addition to club-shaped scavenger cells, known as macrophages, which clean up all that remains of the destroyed tissue.

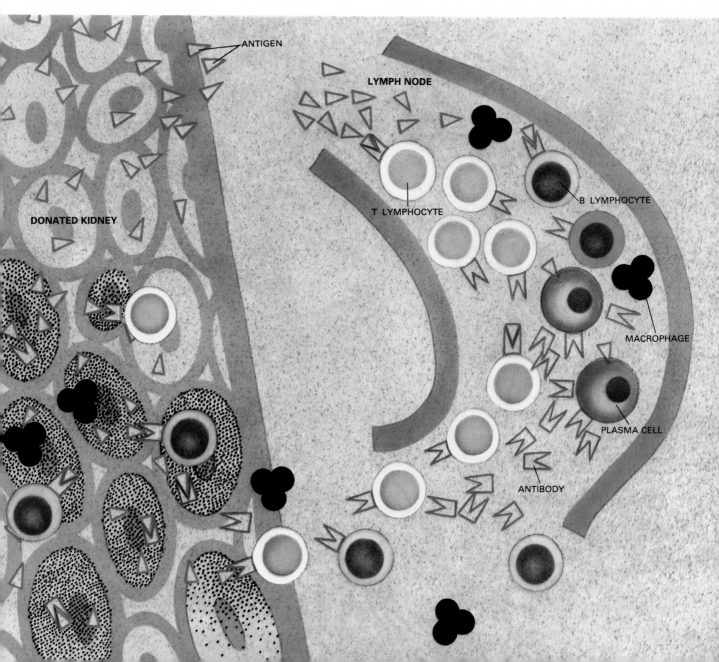

ANTIGEN

LYMPH NODE

DONATED KIDNEY

T LYMPHOCYTE

B LYMPHOCYTE

MACROPHAGE

PLASMA CELL

ANTIBODY

Transplants That Take—Sometimes

In spite of the body's hostility to any donated organ, one transplant procedure has achieved remarkable success. More than 40,000 kidneys have been transplanted since the first in 1954, and in recent years, 90 per cent of those from living donors related to the hosts have kept their new owners alive for at least one year.

A kidney is the organ most often transplanted because a living donor can function on the remaining one of his pair, and because an unsuccessful transplant does not necessarily mean the recipient will die. If the transplant is a failure, the rejected kidney may be removed and the patient put on dialysis until another closely matched kidney becomes available.

Less successful are transplants of organs from deceased donors. The first heart transplant was performed by Dr. Christiaan Barnard in 1967 on 53-year-old Louis Washkansky of Cape Town, South Africa. Though his new heart functioned well for two weeks, he died of pneumonia 18 days after the operation. By the late 1970s, close to 350 heart transplants had been performed, with fair success, throughout the world. A similar number of liver transplants have been made; pancreas transplants, however, remain in the experimental stage.

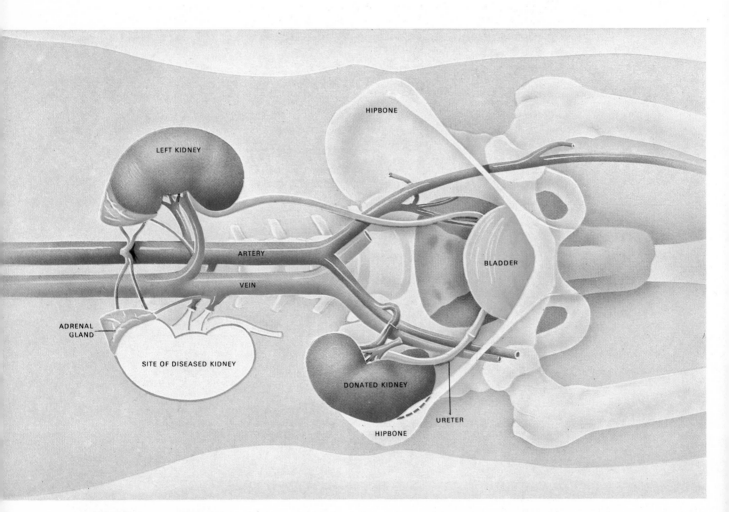

BLUEPRINT FOR A TRANSPLANT
In making a kidney transplant *(above diagram)*, surgeons may remove only one of the patient's diseased kidneys, leaving the adrenal gland intact, and embed the donated kidney against the hipbone—an unnatural site chosen for surgical convenience. Sections of ureter, artery and vein come with the transplanted organ and must be sutured to the host's ureter and blood vessels.

HANGING BY A THREAD
A surgeon holds a donor's kidney in a cloth sling *(opposite)*, preparing to lower it through an incision in the patient's side. Moments before, a second team of surgeons removed the donated organ in an adjoining operating room, placed it in an iced bath and rushed it to the host for transplantation. The whole operation, from incision to sutures, takes about four hours.

134

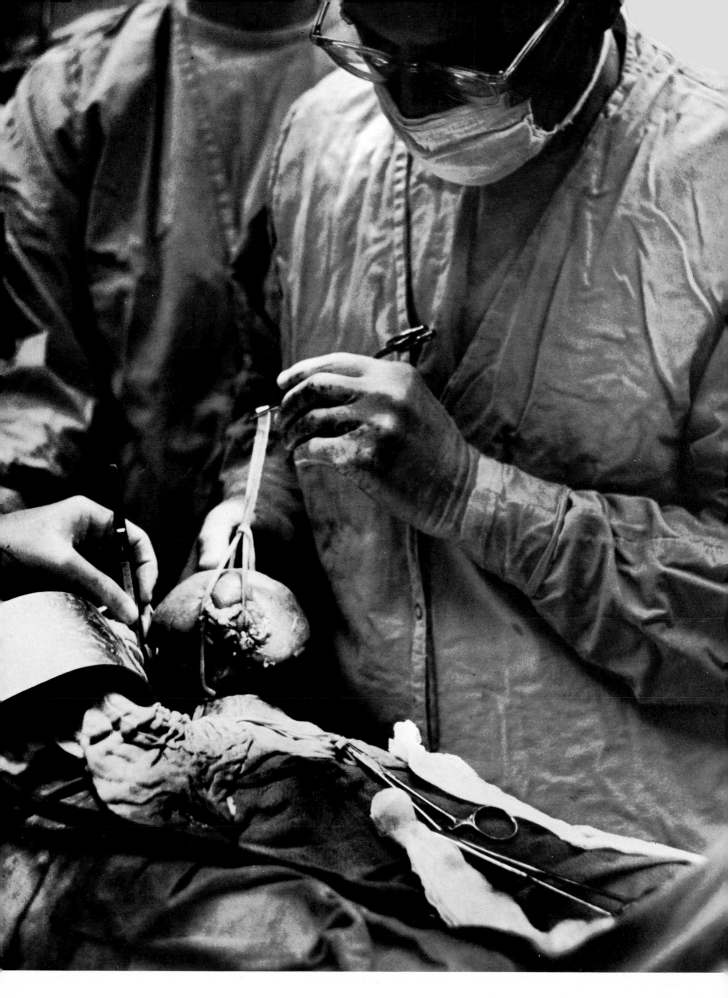

Shoring Up the Body's Defenses

Besides replacing diseased and damaged organs with sound ones, doctors can restore the human immunity system with tissue from the body's most extensive organ—bone marrow.

The pasty tissue in bone cavities produces the lymphocytes which enable the body to fight off infections and germs. Where these cells are absent—a rare genetic disorder called severe combined immune deficiency, or SCID—a person must remain in a sterile environment (*right*) or risk almost certain death. Immunity is also lost when bone marrow has been destroyed, or when it can no longer produce cells, as in aplastic anemia.

The only cure is to transplant new marrow from a donor whose blood cells closely match those of the patient (*below, left*). But close cross matching (*page 132*) is no guarantee of success. Even if the recipient's immune system accepts the transplanted marrow, the lymphocytes of the marrow itself sometimes reject the patient's tissue. The resulting graft-versus-host disease is fatal in up to a third of all bone-marrow transplants.

There is hope, however, since German researchers, working with a few patients, have found they can prevent rejection by infusing extracted marrow with an anti-T-lymphocyte serum before transplanting. Immunosuppressant drugs have also been used to persuade the host to accept the marrow. These substances seem to decrease the production of antibodies hostile to the graft's antigens.

No matter how immunosuppressants are administered, the patient must stay isolated until the marrow produces new blood components and his immune system functions fully.

YOUNG WINNERS IN A DEADLY STRUGGLE
With their natural immunity restored by bone-marrow transplants, two children enjoy a moment with Dr. Richard J. O'Reilly, head of the bone-marrow transplant unit at New York's Memorial Sloane-Kettering Cancer Center. About 200 babies in the United States are born annually with immunological deficiencies, in which normally harmless germs could prove fatal.

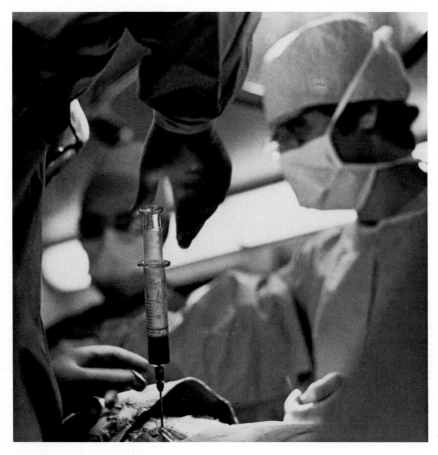

DRAWING OUT THE MARROW
An extra-long hypodermic needle is used to extract bone marrow from the hipbone of a donor. The tissue, found at the honeycomb-like center of the bone, can then be injected into the patient's veins. Within three weeks, the donated marrow will begin producing new blood cells.

LIFE IN A PLASTIC BUBBLE
Wearing a miniature space suit designed for him by NASA, David—the world's longest survivor of SCID—reaches into one of the sterile cubicles where he has lived his entire life. Germfree air generated by a life-support system mounted on a pushcart is pumped into the suit through the 10-foot umbilical cord behind David, which allows him to move around outside the cubicle

An Ounce
of Prevention

Increased understanding of the immune mechanism may soon make tissue transplants common. For hard as it is to overcome an immune reaction, it now seems possible to induce lifelong tolerance to foreign tissues by injecting antigens into a baby's blood —before the body learns to recognize tissues as its own or antigenic.

In the first days of life, the thymus gland *(opposite)* manufactures master lymph cells coded for all the body's own proteins. These master cells are distributed to the bone marrow, the lymph nodes and the spleen, which thereafter serve as seats of antibody production.

In recent experiments *(left)*, mice were injected with antigens before the thymus gland had coded the master lymph cells. These antigens were accepted as though they were the body's own proteins, and no antibodies were produced. And scientists are testing the tolerance of foreign antigens in adult mice. By injecting a mouse with a combination of foreign antigens and its own proteins, scientists can "fool" the recipient's body into believing that the antigen is its own. This procedure makes the body more tolerant of later transplants without making it more susceptible to disease. These techniques have not yet been perfected with human tissues.

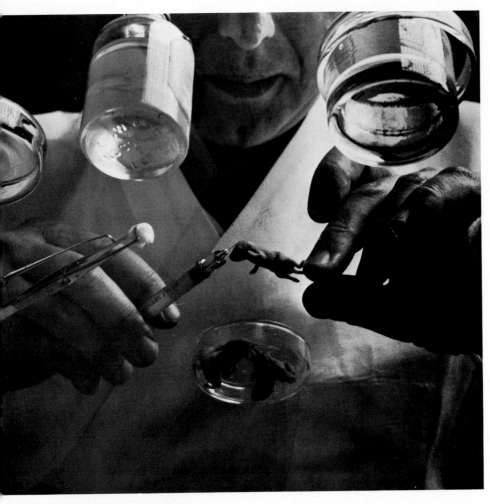

MIXING MOUSE CELLS
Newborn mice of two strains are injected at birth with each other's characteristic antigens. In this case, lymph cells from the spleen are used as antigens. If this is done before the antibody-forming cells have been activated, the mouse can accept the antigens as a part of its own makeup, and later does not reject tissues that are grafted from the donor strain.

IMMUNITY'S INCEPTION
At birth the thymus gland is larger than a baby's fist, as illustrated by the rubber model of the gland shown opposite. Located beneath the breastbone, the thymus early manufactures a master set of antigen-recognizing cells, then it slowly shrivels to about the size of a thumb

BROTHERS UNDER THE SKIN
The white mouse above has accepted a skin graft from a black mouse with which it exchanged spleen cells at birth. Immunologically, the two act like identical twins. In rare cases twin human embryos, although not identical, share a single placenta and the resulting interchange of their bloodstreams enables them to accept grafts from each other in later life.

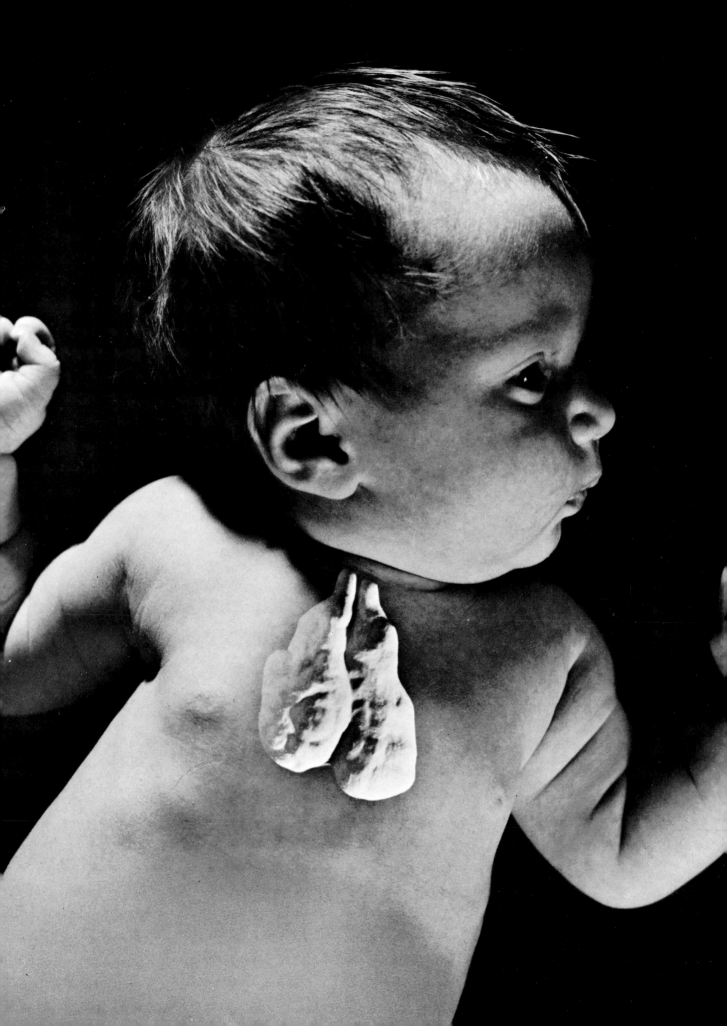

7

A Network
That
Never Sleeps

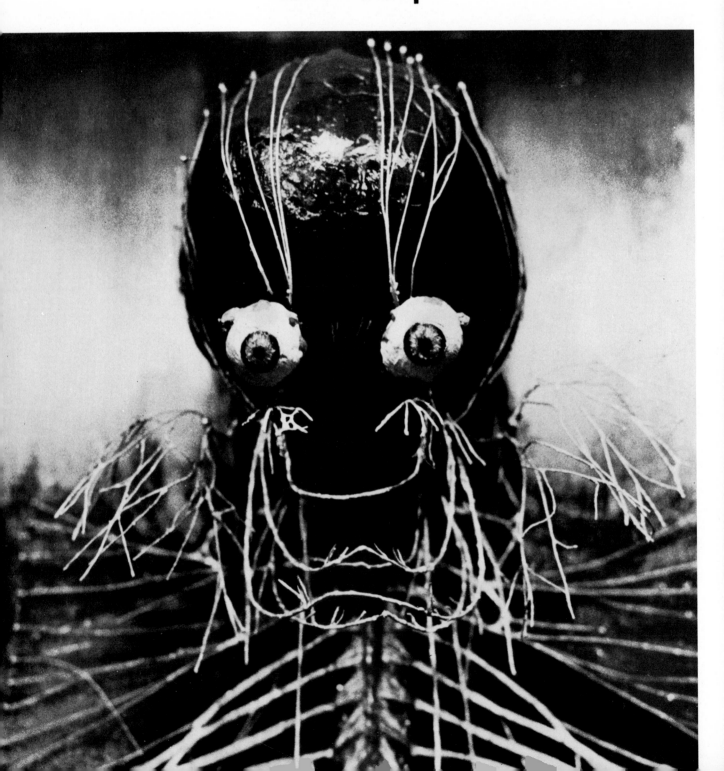

A HORN BLARES, and a child stepping off a curb leaps back to safety as a truck he had not seen thunders past. A housewife slumbers undisturbed through the clamor of her neighbor's television set, but rouses to instant wakefulness at the first whimper from her baby in the adjoining room. A businessman wrestles for days with a problem that seems to defy solution—and then the answer comes to him out of the blue while he is busy thinking about something entirely different.

These are just three examples of the routine, everyday functioning of the human nervous system. Even a thousand examples would not suffice to describe its capabilities. Its presence in the body makes of each of us, in effect, a vast switchboard of humming, flashing, blinking signals constantly sending and receiving messages—some urgent, some not, all concerned with the conduct of the body's affairs. From the moment we are born to the moment we die, this communications network controls our every thought, our every emotion, every step we take, every impression we get. Without it we could not plan, feel, move a muscle, or distinguish between pleasure and pain; we would be deprived of such amenities of life as the enjoyment of food, or music, or the color of a painting, or the pressure of a friendly handshake.

The nervous system, operating by electrochemical impulses, serves the body in a variety of ways. It functions as the body's lookout; as gatherer of information about the world outside us as well as the one within us; as the clearinghouse where this information is processed for instant use or future reference; as general communications center; and as headquarters for mapping the strategy and making the decisions in everything the body does. The nervous system, in short, is the initiator of the body's muscular activity, and the regulator of our mental and physical functions.

This dynamic system of controls is composed of a tissue made up of nerve cells, or neurons, interspersed with other cells, called glia. The brain and the spinal cord serve as the main base of operations for the system. From them a prodigious network of nerves reaches out to every part of the body.

For all its formidable role, the brain has an unprepossessing look. It is soft, gray, and furrowed, and about the size and shape of an acorn squash. All told, it weighs about three pounds. It has a four-inch-long (10-cm), one-inch-wide (2.54-cm) central core, or brainstem, extending upward from the spinal cord. On either side of this core, and behind it, lies a mass of nervous tissue, the cerebellum. Draped over the brainstem and cerebellum is the cerebrum. Its outer layer, the cerebral cortex, is folded and convoluted to fit into the six-by-eight-inch (15-by-20-cm) vault of the skull; if flattened out, the cortex would cover more than two square feet (2 m^2) in area. A fissure down the middle divides the cerebrum into two

A MEMORABLE LEGACY
This forest of nerves, with its gleaming eyes, is a portion of the remains of a Philadelphia scrubwoman who willed her body to science almost 100 years ago. Each nerve, painstakingly removed from the cadaver, was painted white for display. The area shown is but a fraction of the complex nervous system that rules all body activities, from wiggling toes to creating ideas.

hemispheres connected by glistening bands, much lighter in color than the gray exterior tissue. Here, as elsewhere in the nervous system, the two colors represent a significant difference. The gray matter is made up of gray nerve-cell bodies. The white matter is made up of nerve fibers—axons—which extend from the cell bodies and are capable of conducting nerve impulses. What gives these fibers their color, as well as a generally waxy look, is a fatty coating, myelin, which not only insulates the fiber but also makes it a speedier conductor.

The spinal cord, which is about 18 inches (46 cm) long, resembles a cable tapered at both ends; at its widest, it is a little more than half an inch across. Like the brain, the spinal cord contains both gray and white matter; the gray nerve-cell bodies form a column in the center of the cord, sheathed by the white bundles of nerve fibers. Surrounding the cord on the outside is a perforated tunnel of bone formed by the rings of the vertebrae—the body's backbone.

A reach from tip to toe

The network of nerves which threads the body is rooted both in the brain and in the spinal cord. From the brain, nerve fibers converge to form 12 pairs of so-called cranial nerves serving the head, eyes, ears, throat, and some organs in the chest and abdomen. From the spinal cord 31 pairs of nerves pass out through openings between the vertebrae at various levels. From the upper part of the cord some of these nerves branch and rebranch to form nerve trunks leading to the upper torso, arms and hands. From the lower part of the cord other nerves branch and rebranch to form nerve trunks leading to the pelvis, thighs, legs and feet. The nerves reach every square millimeter of skin, every muscle, every blood vessel, every bone—every part of the body from tip to toe. And each of these nerves carries impulses—electrochemical signals—that are triggered by some stimulus.

The basic unit of the nervous system—the neuron—has one structural characteristic which distinguishes it from all other types of body cells. From the central part of the neuron thin fibers extend like delicate tendrils. Depending upon their location and function neurons may be anywhere from a fraction of an inch to as much as five or six feet long (the longest reaches from the base of the brain to the big toe). It is via their fibers that the neurons perform their unique function of transmitting signals to and from the brain and spinal cord. Upon receiving a signal, one neuron sends it on to another neuron lying adjacent to it across a kind of "spark gap" called a synapse. Thus the neurons form an entire chain, like a bucket brigade. From various parts of the body via the spinal cord or directly to the brain go signals which produce sensations of sight, sound, pain, pressure, touch, heat or cold. Back from the brain or the spinal cord

THE BACKBONE OF THE NERVOUS SYSTEM

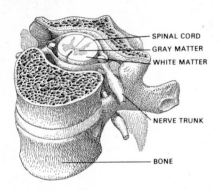

SPINAL CORD
GRAY MATTER
WHITE MATTER

NERVE TRUNK

BONE

A WELL-SHEATHED CABLE
From the lower vertebrae to the brain runs a communication cable that makes modern microcircuitry cumbersome in comparison. The spinal cord is wrapped in three layers of protective membranes, with fluid between two of the layers, and the whole encased in the heavy bone of the spine *(above)*, making it almost impervious to injuries. Nerve impulses travel to and fro between it and the outer reaches of the body via 31 pairs of nerve trunks. The cord itself *(below)* is an elliptical column of white and gray matter. The white matter contains sensory nerves *(striped area)* leading to the brain and motor nerves *(dark area)* from the brain; the gray matter contains a gelatinous mass of connecting neurons.

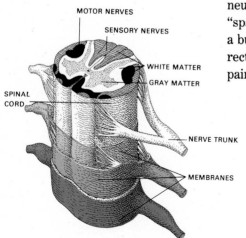

MOTOR NERVES
SENSORY NERVES

WHITE MATTER
GRAY MATTER

SPINAL CORD

NERVE TRUNK

MEMBRANES

go "orders"—motor signals—to muscles in the fingers, toes, heart, intestines and elsewhere.

There are three general classes of neurons, grouped according to their function. Sensory neurons carry signals to the spinal cord and brain. Motor neurons carry directives from the brain and spinal cord, both to stimulate the contraction or relaxation of muscles and to spur the activity of glands. Finally, connecting neurons—interneurons—shuttle the signals back and forth, through complex pathways, between the brain, spinal cord and other parts of the body. Interneurons constitute over 99 per cent of the more than 10 billion neurons in the nervous system, including most of the nerve cells of the brain itself.

The sensory neurons keep the brain informed of what is happening outside and inside the body through a variety of sensory pick-up units called receptors. Some of these, lying at or near the skin surface, may be specially sensitive to tissue damage (causing pain), or light contact (producing a touch sensation), or pressure, or temperature, either hot or cold. Other receptors on the tongue and in the nose respond to chemicals that produce tastes and odors. In the retina of the eye, rodlike receptors respond to light of varying intensities, while conelike receptors respond to color. Receptors in the ear respond to minute vibrations caused by sound waves striking the eardrum. Other receptors are embedded deep in the walls of the intestines; when the intestines contract vigorously because of the presence of indigestible food or gas, these receptors transmit waxing and waning signals of pain, which are interpreted as cramps. Still other receptors lodged in muscles, ligaments and tendons fire off signals to the brain any time a muscle contracts or a joint moves or is subjected to added pressure or tension.

The sizzling steak stimulus

All the varied sensory stimuli picked up by the receptors must be converted into signals before they can be transmitted anywhere. In every case the signal is of the same kind—an electrochemical impulse. Depending on the type of stimulus, the conversion is set off in one of two ways. If the stimulus is mechanical—the touch of a pin on the skin, an impinging sound wave or a stretching of the intestinal wall—the nerve endings are, so to speak, pinched; this action initiates the impulse. If the stimulus is chemical—as when aromatic vapors from a sizzling steak encounter the smell receptors in the nose, or when light causes changes in the rods and cones of the retina—the chemical reaction alone triggers the impulse.

Whether the stimulus is mechanical or chemical, the impulse travels as a sort of electrochemical wave of activity, passing along the nerve at the rate of anywhere from one to 350 feet per second (0.3 to 106 m per sec.).

The speed depends on the size and type of the particular nerve fiber and the thickness of the coating of myelin around it. Certain fibers which lack myelin are comparatively slow transmitters.

We tend to think of a nerve stimulus only in terms of warnings of danger—a stab of pain, for instance, or a flash of bright light, or a clanging bell. Actually, we receive sensory stimuli all the time, whether danger impends or not. During a deep sleep, for example, we would not continue breathing unless specially sensitive receptors in the circulatory system signaled the brain of an increase in the level of carbon dioxide in the blood. But there is no basic difference between the signals of stabbing pain from a pricked finger and the steady flow of unperceived impulses that maintain breathing. The major difference lies in where these impulses start, how they are interpreted, what portion of the nervous system they involve, and the effects they produce.

Each sensory receptor usually responds only to its own particular kind of stimulus. A pain receptor which is lying side by side with touch receptors will, under ordinary circumstances, respond only to tissue damage. Occasionally, however, when the stimuli are exceptionally strong, they can excite receptors that are not usually sensitive to them. Receptors in the retina, for example, normally respond only to visual stimuli. But sensations of flashing light can also be triggered by pressure on the eyeball.

Sensations in tandem

Several types of receptors acting in combination can produce more complex sensory experiences. We may find a particular food palatable or unpalatable, for example, not only because of how it tastes and smells, but also because of how it appeals to the eye. We may simultaneously experience sensations of touch, pressure, heat and pain in lifting a pot from the stove.

While the sensory neurons are bringing in information from all parts of the body to the brain, motor neurons are at the same time carrying directions from the brain to the muscles—signals which prod them into activity. The fibers of these neurons terminate in tiny flat plates—so-called "motor end plates"—which lie in close contact with individual muscle fibers. Here the nerve ending is separated from the muscle only by a tiny gap.

Even this minute space would stop motor signals in their tracks except for a special chemical reaction that takes place at the gap. As the impulse reaches the motor end plate, the nerve ending releases a chemical substance known as acetylcholine, which acts as a neurotransmitter in initiating events in the muscle cell. With the muscle's contraction, another substance—an enzyme called cholinesterase—begins breaking down the

SENSORY NERVE ENDINGS

NERVE FIBER

CELL BODY

SENSORY NEURON

TERMINALS

INTERNEURON

MUSCLE FIBERS

MOTOR NEURON

MOTOR NERVE ENDINGS

THE ROUTE OF A SIMPLE REFLEX
The impulses of a nerve reflex, from initial stimulus to contraction of a muscle, are conveyed by neurons—each having a cell body, nerve fiber and fiber endings. A stimulus at the endings of a sensory neuron triggers impulses which race along the nerve fiber, through the cell body to terminals in the spinal cord. There an interneuron transmits the impulses to a motor neuron. The process ends in the muscle, which contracts as ordered.

accumulated acetylcholine and clearing it away so the next arriving nerve impulse can set the cycle in motion again. It is this rechargeable chemical cycle that effectively bridges the gap between motor nerve ending and muscle cell so that muscle action can be stimulated.

Determining which muscles contract and which relax in the continuous adjustments required to maintain our body's balance and keep us upright is a function of the lower-echelon centers of the brain—the brainstem and cerebellum. These also control our respiration and rate of heartbeat, and perform a multitude of other essential maintenance jobs. Somewhat higher echelons of the brain regulate body temperature, appetite, and such complex motor activities as walking, running and reaching for objects. The highest echelon of the brain—the cerebral cortex—allows us to have our awareness of sight and sound, as well as the delicate sensations of weight, texture and form. It also makes possible the experiencing of emotions such as fear and anger, and enables us to feel pleasure or pain.

The site of sophistication

The cerebral cortex—the general staff of the nervous system, so to speak—does the most sophisticated processing of incoming signals. It puts together stimuli from many sources, integrating them, interpreting them and storing them for future reference. It also designs and initiates the equally complex responses of the body. The cortex is responsible for decision-making, and is thus involved in all of our conscious intellectual functions, such as thinking, worrying, planning ahead and solving problems of every sort.

A great deal about the activity of the brain is still imperfectly understood, and indeed it is only within the past decade or so that a plausible explanation has been found for one of the most baffling operations of the nervous system: the way in which an electrochemical impulse travels along a nerve fiber. In the early 1950s two Britishers, Alan Lloyd Hodgkin and Andrew Fielding Huxley, propounded an ingenious theory to explain the mechanism involved (some of the experiments involved were performed on the squid, whose giant nerve fibers are about 50 times as thick as mammalian nerve fibers and hence easier to work with). The work was later supplemented by that of an Australian, Sir John Carew Eccles. By 1963 such a wealth of evidence supported their ideas that all three were jointly awarded a Nobel Prize in medicine for their work.

In essence the theory holds that a nerve impulse, once started at the end of a nerve fiber, is kicked along by a series of electrical nudges. The process is so extremely fast that one fiber can boost along up to 1,000 separate impulses in a single second, pausing after each has passed before handling the next. All this occurs as a result of a fleeting change in the

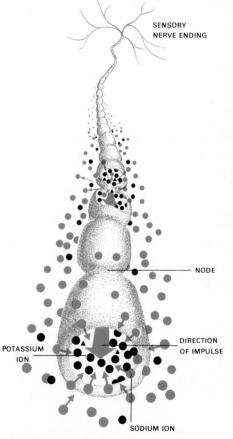

SENSORY NERVE ENDING

NODE

DIRECTION OF IMPULSE

POTASSIUM ION

SODIUM ION

THE POWER PLANT OF NERVES
A nerve impulse is a self-perpetuating series of electrical charges along an insulated nerve fiber. The fiber, surrounded by positive sodium ions, has potassium ions in its negative interior. Whenever a sensory nerve ending is stimulated, the sodium is temporarily admitted into the nerve at a node—a break in the insulation. The resulting electrical charge sets off a chain of charges extending from node to node to the central nervous system.

145

cell membrane of the nerve fiber. Ordinarily the membrane serves as a barrier between two concentrations of electrically charged ions—potassium ions inside the nerve fiber and sodium ions in the body fluid outside it. But when a nerve impulse is set off—by a sound receptor in the ear, for example—the cell membrane briefly alters to allow charged potassium ions to flow out of the cell and charged sodium ions to flow in. This back-and-forth shuttling creates a tiny electrical potential, which constitutes the nerve impulse. When enough potential builds up at the nerve endings, the next cell is excited. Once the impulse has passed, the cell membrane resumes its role as barrier—until another impulse turns up.

A time for problem-solving

The complicated and busy nervous system consumes energy at an astounding rate. Nerve cells, therefore, require far more fuel—oxygen and glucose—than other cells; thus they must have a continuous and rich supply of blood or they will quickly die. Nerve cells in the brain alone use up as much as 20 per cent of all the oxygen available in the adult body, for they are working at frantic speed 24 hours a day. This may seem curious, since we think of sleep as "giving the brain a rest." But the brain is indisputably active during sleep periods. Quite aside from maintaining breathing and the rate of heartbeat, the brain may function during these periods to try to search out answers to particularly difficult problems and to reconsider experiences of the day that were flowing in too fast to be dealt with carefully at the time.

By night or day, the brain's need for blood-borne oxygen never flags. Normally, during the course of every 24 hours, we lose some neurons simply because they wear out and die. Fortunately great numbers would have to die to produce any noticeable effect, but the small losses inevitably accumulate. Neurologists today believe that the insidious loss of mental efficiency that occurs in old age—the process we call senility—is a direct result of day-by-day destruction of a few neurons here and there, until the total loss begins to mount up and is accelerated by narrowing of blood vessels to the brain. Whatever the cause of the loss, once a neuron is destroyed it is destroyed. No new nerve cell will ever take its place; a year-old baby has all the neurons it will ever have. If only a nerve fiber is cut, and the cell itself is not killed, a new fiber may eventually grow out along the course of the cut fiber. But if the nucleus of the neuron is destroyed, the cell is gone forever. Such diseases as poliomyelitis cause paralysis because they destroy nerve nuclei which serve the muscle fibers, so that the muscles can never again receive directive impulses. The muscles atrophy, and the damage is permanent, even if the victim fights off the polio virus and survives.

Because the body could not tolerate the loss of too many neurons, and because nervous tissue is innately fragile, the nervous system operates behind an impressive wall of protection. The brain is encased in the tough armor plate of the skull. The spinal cord is enclosed in a strong but flexible bony sheath made up of the vertebrae. Both brain and spinal cord, furthermore, are surrounded by a clear cerebrospinal fluid which serves, among other purposes, as a shock absorber.

The rest of the nervous system is also well protected. The nerve trunks throughout the body are deeply buried between layers of muscle, except in such rare places as the point where the ulnar nerve crosses the elbow just beneath the skin—the easily shockable "funny bone." Many of the delicate receptor endings of sensory nerves are also carefully shielded. The nerve endings in the retina lie at the back of the eye, which is buried in a deep bony socket; they are protected from too much light by the self-adjusting cameralike diaphragm of the iris. Sound receptors are encased deep within the ear in tiny bony caverns in the skull. Certain receptors—those sensitive to pain, touch, heat and cold, which lie at or near the surface of the skin—are relatively exposed. They are so widely distributed, however, that the loss of a few here and there is not really important.

Under this massive cloak of protection, the nervous system conducts its complex activities with brilliant dispatch. Nerve impulses are transmitted so rapidly that a whole sequence of actions, interpretations and responses can take place before we are even aware that anything has happened. Indeed, a single stimulus may fire off thousands upon thousands of responses within a fraction of a second.

The nuances of a nicked finger

Consider, for example, the train of events after we accidentally nick a finger while slicing bread. First, this injury stimulates a protective reflex action by which the pain signal from the finger triggers motor nerves in the spinal cord, instantaneously forcing us to jerk our hand back before word of the injury gets to the brain. The pain stimulus is also picked up by interneurons in the spinal cord, so that news of the cut finger (and of the reflex response) is simultaneously "echoed" to the brain, setting off a chain reaction in seconds. Here, in rough chronological order, are but a few of the many signals that fly to and from the brain during this reaction, and the ways in which we may deal with them:

Involuntary exclamation (set off by signals to speech areas of brain): Ouch!

Awareness (as cerebral cortex receives report of sudden movements): Something happened and I jerked my hand away from the breadboard.

Heightened awareness (as other signals reach the cortex and are interpreted as pain): Whatever it was, it hurts.

THE VERTEBRATE BRAIN
The brains of all vertebrates—from the frog to man—have the same basic parts: the medulla controls such involuntary activities as respiration; the cerebellum maintains balance and posture; the thalamus acts as a message-relay center. The differences in brain power that we call intelligence are related to variations in the size and complexity of the cerebrum, the seat of reason. A frog, which operates mostly by reflex, or involuntary, actions, will be little changed if its cerebrum is removed. But deprive man of his cerebrum, and his ability to function will be completely destroyed. The particular seat of intelligence in the cerebrum seems to be the thin outer rind, or cortex. A biological rule of thumb seems to be: the more complex the cortex the more intelligent the animal. In man its expansion has heaped it into deep folds and convolutions.

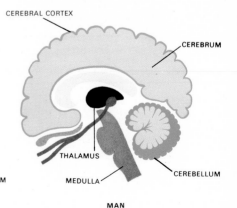

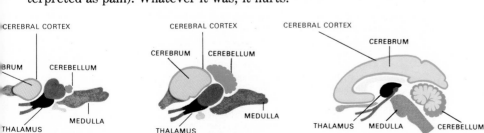

FROG

GOOSE

MONKEY

MAN

147

Questions (generated by complex patterns of signals within cortex): What was it? Any damage done?

Purposeful response (as cortex sifts information): Lift up the finger and look at it.

Observation (as cortex processes data): It's bleeding; obviously it's cut.

Evaluation (in wake of data processing): Not too bad; just a nick.

Sensation of relief (also in wake of data processing): No need to worry.

Orders (unconscious): All right, heart, slow down. Adrenals, relax.

Orders (conscious): Okay, find some antiseptic and a bandage; wrap up the finger; get back to making the sandwiches.

Storage of data for future use: Item—check any knife for sharpness before you use it; item—that's what a nicked finger feels like; item—don't panic next time over a few drops of blood.

This silent soliloquy barely hints at the flurry of activity instigated by a minor accident. Many other reactions may be stirred up as well: self-annoyance at responding so excitedly to a superficial injury, frustration at not being able to hit back at the knife, relief that the cut didn't go any deeper, and so on. The really amazing aspect of this innocuous accident is the sheer volume of information sifted in its wake by the brain, and the remarkable speed with which the sifting occurs.

Home-grown pain control

An even more complex picture of how the brain operates has emerged in recent years. For one thing, scientists now are convinced that the brain has the remarkable capacity to block out pain. The first breakthrough came in the early 1970s, when studies showed that morphine—long known to be a potent pain killer—produces its effects by interacting with specific molecular sites in the brain, much as various hormones do *(Chapter 8)*. The researchers hypothesized that these sites—called opiate receptors—must be there for good reason. But what were they doing embracing the likes of an addictive drug such as morphine? The only plausible explanation, researchers concluded, was that the narcotic duplicated the action of a pain-killing substance inherent in the brain.

These suspicions were confirmed in late 1975, when two such molecular configurations were discovered in pig brains. Dubbed enkephalins (from the Greek for "in the head"), the substances turned out to be short chains of amino acids called peptides, similar to those already known to effect the release of hormones from the pituitary gland. Although the precise mechanism will take years to work out, the enkephalins may play a prominent role in physiologically induced analgesia. Further evidence suggests that these and other newly discovered peptide substances are also important in controlling a wide range of bodily functions, including reproduction, eating, drinking and even memory.

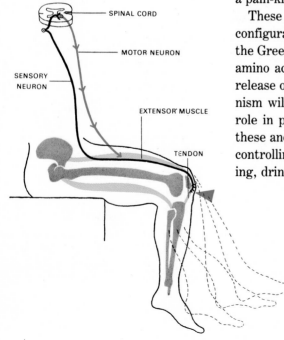

SPINAL CORD

MOTOR NEURON

SENSORY NEURON

EXTENSOR MUSCLE

TENDON

MECHANISM OF THE KNEE REFLEX
When a doctor taps a knee tendon, he activates one of the few two-neuron reflex arcs in the body. The blow stretches the extensor muscle, and a sensory neuron relays this information to the spinal cord. Here a motor neuron is automatically stimulated to counteract the stretch. But the motor neuron normally overcompensates, causing the extensor muscle to contract sharply and jerk the foot forward in an involuntary kick.

Taken as a whole, the nervous system provides an incredibly rich mass of information for the body about its internal and external environment. Indeed, recent experiments indicate that we depend strongly —perhaps for our very sanity—upon a constant flow of impressions from the outside world. Volunteers in such experiments, when deprived of these contacts for only a few hours—by being blindfolded, for instance, and suspended in a tank of warm, gently flowing water—quickly began to develop fantastic daydreams or even hallucinations. Some lost their sense of time; others heard singing choruses; others developed a confused sense of taste, mistaking the bologna they were fed for ham. For the most part, however, the hallucinations were visual. One man was convinced that he was seeing a herd of pink, blue, and purple elephants; another believed that he was seeing a hippopotamus charging out of an instrument case; still another insisted that a small nearby shelf was crammed with grayish black socks.

The undetected sneaks

However, the impressions which we receive from the world around us are limited to those for which we have sensory receptors. Certain dangers can sneak undetected past this early warning system. Overexposure to the sun may lead to a disabling sunburn, yet the body has no indication of danger, for we have no receptors to detect an excess of ultraviolet light. Foreign proteins to which the body is sensitive can enter the bloodstream; we may have no hint of trouble, though these proteins may cause shock or even death. Fortunately such occurrences are rare.

In addition to those parts of the nervous system through which the voluntary activities are controlled, the body has an auxiliary network of nervous tissue which provides nerves for the smooth muscle of the blood vessel walls, the digestive tract, the lungs and the heart. It also influences glandular secretions. Called the autonomic (self-governing) nervous system, this network is largely concerned with regulation of the unconscious, involuntary body functions—such as respiration and digestion—which must be carried on day or night regardless of any awareness or desire. Yet, the distinction between the voluntary and involuntary nervous systems—a time-honored fundamental of physiology—is becoming blurred, as researchers train selected subjects to apply their will to regulate such "involuntary" functions as blood pressure and heart rate.

Nerve cells of the autonomic system, before they connect with interneurons in the spinal cord, converge in a series of field stations called ganglia, which are imbedded, among other places, near or within the organs of the abdomen and thorax. The autonomic nerves and ganglia join together into small networks, or plexuses, which connect with the involuntary control centers of the brain by way of various nerve trunks.

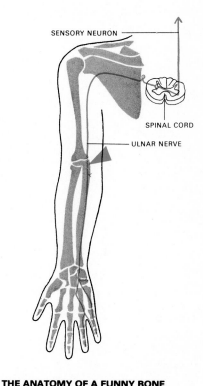

THE ANATOMY OF A FUNNY BONE
The unsettling shock that reverberates in the fingers and courses up the spinal cord to the brain when the back of the elbow is struck is really a nerve impulse, originating not in a bone but in the ulnar nerve. This nerve extends the entire length of the arm and is well protected everywhere except at that one tender spot. (The misleading term "funny bone" may have stemmed from a word play on "humerus," the large bone in the upper arm.)

Perhaps the most celebrated of these networks—particularly to aficionados of the prizefight—is the solar plexus at the pit of the stomach. Other autonomic impulses travel directly from the brain or spinal cord by nerves such as the vagus nerve, serving the stomach and upper digestive tract. Generally speaking, however, we are unaware of the existence of this auxiliary nerve network.

All but the most primitive animal organisms have a nervous system of some sort, but in man it has reached a higher level of development than in any other creature on earth. With a brain small enough to be operating on the amount of power that would be needed to burn a 10-watt bulb, man's nervous system in some ways is thousands of times more capable than the most complex calculating machine. Man's comparatively large cerebral cortex gives him better memory, better judgment and better reasoning ability than any other creature. It permits him to make quicker and more accurate decisions. It provides him with the ability to communicate by speech, to leap intuitively to conclusions that are not clearly indicated by the information he has on hand, and to moderate his body's fight-or-flight reactions by superimposing on primitive emotions such controls as love, joy, understanding, a sense of wonder and a capability for introspection. Above all, it has given man his unique awareness of his own intelligence.

The Sense Organs: Reporters of the Outside World

The human body is, among other things, a highly tuned instrument for the perception of the external world. Vivid reports pour into man's brain through his eyes, ears, skin, nose and mouth, describing in detail the variety of things on earth. A sense of balance orients him to the earth itself. He may have other sources of information, little understood as yet, sometimes called extrasensory perception. Just as it is impossible to conceive of the human head without eyes and ears, so it is impossible to conceive of a meaningful life that does not partake of the world through the senses. Experiences undergone by men in solitary confinement show that a human deprived of the external world cannot stand the effect; it is disturbing then terrifying—and at last the prisoner hallucinates the world he needs. To be sure, senses can mislead us, as when we see optical illusions. There are also more things on earth than our traditional five senses perceive: radio waves and gamma rays, for example. But in spite of their limitations, it is the senses that have made man the master of his environment, and the beneficiary of its wonder.

A

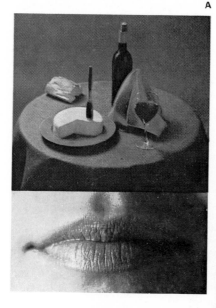

D

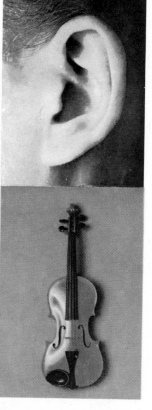

C

B

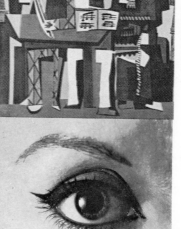

E

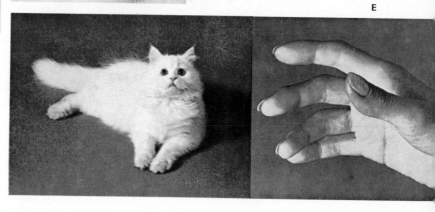

THE SCIENCE OF SENSING
The simple but abundant pleasure of tasting,
smelling, seeing, hearing and touching
can be described solely in terms of chemistry
and physics: wine and cheese in the mouth
(A) release chemicals which provoke the
taste buds; cells behind the nose are chemically
affected by molecules emanating from a rose
(B). The eye senses different wavelengths
reflected from Picasso's *Three Musicians* (C);
the funnel of the external ear catches air
waves set off by a violin string (D); and
the skin of the hand has thousands of nerve
endings which react to the fur of a kitten (E).
So lightning-fast is the nervous system
that in all these cases we are unaware
of neural processes; we only enjoy.

HEADING

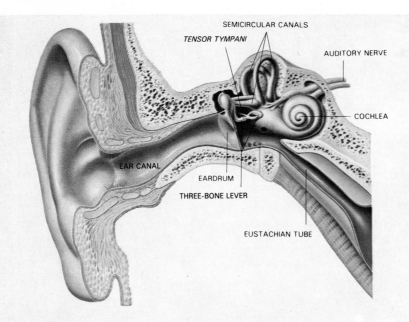

SEMICIRCULAR CANALS

TENSOR TYMPANI

AUDITORY NERVE

COCHLEA

EAR CANAL

EARDRUM

THREE-BONE LEVER

EUSTACHIAN TUBE

Tiny Taps on a Delicate Drum

The human ear is buffeted by stimuli from every direction—from around corners and through walls. Man hears sounds when any vibrating object pushes air molecules at a rate between 16 and 28,000 vibrations per second. The waves enter the ear canal and strike the eardrum *(left)*. The drum's vibrations travel through the middle ear, along a three-bone lever which triples the pressure of the vibrations. These bones pass it to a membrane, the oval window, behind the third bone. The window sends waves through the fluid of the snail-shaped cochlea, agitating hairs which transmit messages along the auditory nerve to the brain. There the stimulation at the end of the chain is heard as sound of a certain pitch and volume.

INNER FORTRESS
The sensitive parts of the ear are inside the skull. The fragile eardrum is protected by a muscle, the *tensor tympani,* which dampens dangerously loud noises, and by the Eustachian tube, an opening to the nose and throat which equalizes the air pressure on both sides of the drum. The semicircular canals are nonauditory organs which control balance *(pages 162-163).*

OUTER EAR   **MIDDLE EAR**   **INNER EAR**

A MECHANICAL EAR
The fanciful contraption above reconstructs the mechanical processes involved in hearing. Sound waves *(arrows)* from the bell vibrate a disklike eardrum (A) and a three-piece lever (B), which produces waves in the fluid of the cochlea (C). The small pipe (D) is the Eustachian tube. No existing machine operates in this fashion; telephones transmit sound as electrical impulses.

In a natural gesture, a woman shuts off the extraneous sounds entering one ear to listen to her husband's voice on the telephone.

SIGHT

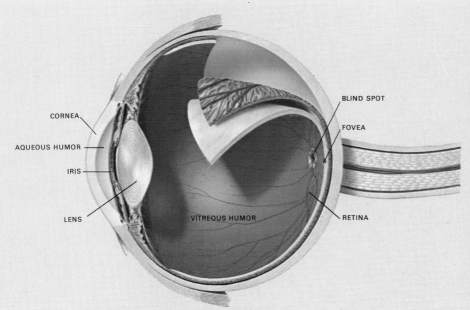

CORNEA

AQUEOUS HUMOR

IRIS

LENS

BLIND SPOT

FOVEA

VITREOUS HUMOR

RETINA

Window on a Colorful World

Light waves are readily blocked, and the eyes, unlike the ears, must be aimed at what they see. The eye operates on the same principle as the camera—the only machine directly modeled on a sense organ. The eye, however, takes two simultaneous pictures, one in black and white, the other in color. Cells in the retina, called rods, register black and white only; they are so sensitive they can detect light as feeble as a 100-trillionth of a watt. Other retinal cells, the cones, are affected by color, and are most abundant at the fovea, the place where the image falls when the eye focuses. The blind spot, lacking both rods and cones, is where the optic nerve leaves the retina, carrying its pictures for the brain to develop.

NATURAL CAMERA

Cushioned by fat, gently jiggling in its protective bony socket, the human eye is at work every waking moment, effortlessly shifting its focus from one distance to another by changing the curvature of its lens. The jellylike vitreous humor helps maintain the eye's shape, the watery aqueous humor nourishes the cornea and lens. The iris controls the admission of light.

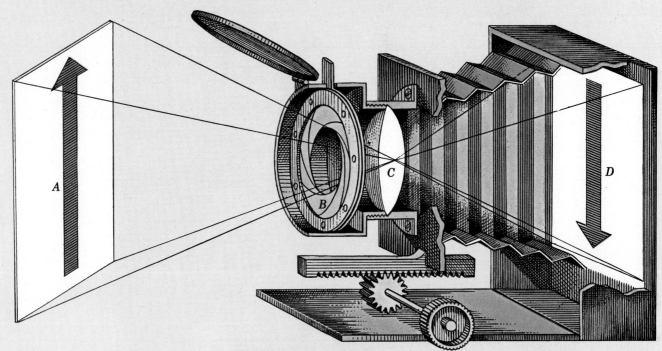

MAN-MADE EYE

In old-fashioned cameras like the one above, a diaphragm (B) is in front of the lens (C). The diaphragm, like the iris of an eye, has an opening with a variable diameter for regulating the amount of light allowed to strike the film. An upside-down and reversed image (D) of the object (A) also appears on the retina of a human eye; it is righted in the darkroom of the mind.

Watching a flaming match, a child flexes tiny eye muscles to adjust the curvature of his lenses, causing the object to spring into focus.

TOUCH

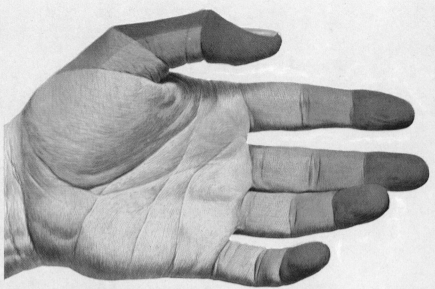

Tidings from Close at Hand

The body's six pounds (2.7 kg) of skin, thinned out like pie dough, with an average thickness of one twentieth of an inch (0.13 cm), hold a mantle of nerve endings. No other perceptions of the outer world are as intimate as the skin's tidings of warmth, softness, chill or pain. Sensations of touch are more complex than sight or hearing because most are mixtures of several stimuli. Feeling a handful of soil (*opposite*) reveals its density, texture, dampness, and the size and hardness of its particles. Each of these is reducible to two or more of the five basic skin stimuli: contact, pressure, cold, heat and pain. The dampness, for example, like wetness in general, is fundamentally a sensation of coldness.

THE TOUCHINESS OF FINGERTIPS
The human hand, designed for grasping and for touching, has up to 1,300 nerve endings per square inch. The shading in the picture above shows the varying degrees of sensitivity in the palm and three areas of the fingers. The fingertips are more sensitive than any part of the body except the lips, tongue and tip of nose, and are twice as sensitive as other parts of the hand.

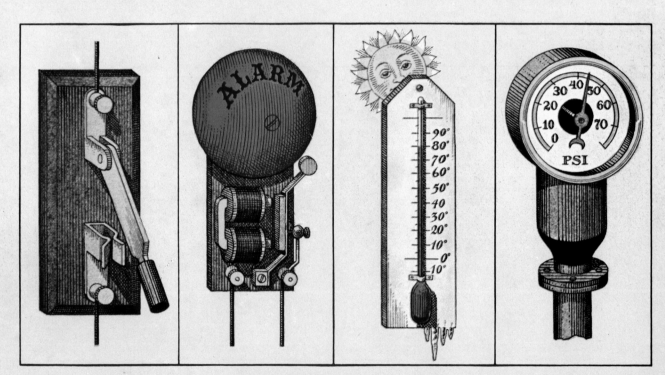

A REGISTER OF SENSATIONS
The devices above symbolize the brain's reception center for touch sensations, where the component stimuli are measured for their intensity. The electric switch represents contact, the alarm bell pain, the thermometer both hot and cold, the pressure gauge weight or pressure. Combinations of these five stimuli make possible an infinite variety of touch sensations.

In the trained hand of a farmer, the feel of earth is a variety of basic touch sensations that enables him to judge the quality of the soil.

SMELL

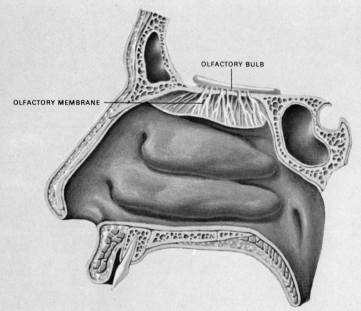

OLFACTORY BULB

OLFACTORY MEMBRANE

Poignant, Powerful and Fleeting

Man's sense of smell is weak compared to that of other animals, and he does not depend on it nearly so much as on sight, hearing and touch. Nevertheless, odors can seem to him both poignant and powerful. They are closely related to tastes. Most foods with marked flavors—wine, cocoa, vanilla, oranges—stimulate essentially by their aromas.

The chemistry and physics of smell are not well defined, but one recent classification considers every odor a blend of four primary smells—fragrant, acid, rancid and burnt. If the primary smells could be measured on an arbitrary scale of eight points *(below)*, every odor on earth could be given a distinctive number based on the strength of its constituents.

MOLECULES IN A CUL-DE-SAC

In a small dead-end passage of the nasal cavity *(above)*, thousands of tiny hairs wave back and forth in the thin film of mucus that covers the olfactory membrane. When air is sniffed, it eddies into this cul-de-sac and dissolves in the mucus. The odorous molecules immediately stimulate the hairs to send signals to the olfactory bulb, which in turn relays them to the brain.

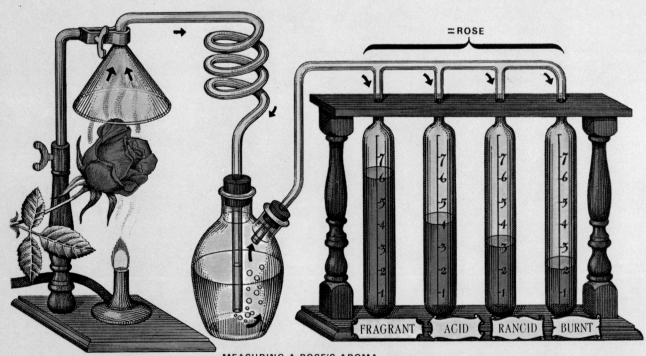

= ROSE

FRAGRANT   ACID   RANCID   BURNT

MEASURING A ROSE'S AROMA

In this laboratory version of how man smells, the odorous molecules of a rose, agitated by warmth, enter the funnel and eddy down to the flask. There they are dissolved, as in the olfactory membrane and its mucus. The test tubes note the component smells that make up the aroma of a rose: strongly fragrant, moderately acid, somewhat rancid and only slightly burnt.

If the man above sniffs the roses too long, he will no longer smell them; reaction to any odor soon lessens, making way for new smells.

TASTE

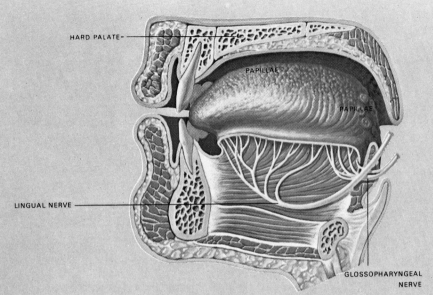

HARD PALATE

PAPILLAE

PAPILLAE

LINGUAL NERVE

GLOSSOPHARYNGEAL
NERVE

PUSHING FOR THE LAST DROP
The tongue *(above)* pushes food against the hard palate in the process of chewing. Molecules of food dissolve in saliva, and the fluid reaches the bud-shaped clusters of cells, called taste buds, in the lining of the tongue's papillae. The buds in the front and middle of the tongue signal the brain via the lingual nerve; those in the rear via the glossopharyngeal nerve.

An Elusive Mixture on the Tongue

Taste is the least informative of the senses. An infant is born with taste buds throughout his mouth; by adulthood most have disappeared, with those remaining mostly concentrated on the tongue. With such a depleted army of scouts, the brain often needs supporting evidence from smell, sight and touch to know what the mouth is tasting; a blindfolded person with a cold cannot distinguish between orange juice *(opposite)* and grapefruit juice. Taste sensations have been analyzed as blends of four primary tastes *(below):* sweet, sour, bitter and salty. Sweetness and saltiness are detected mostly by the buds at the tip of the tongue; the sides are most sensitive to sourness, the back to bitterness.

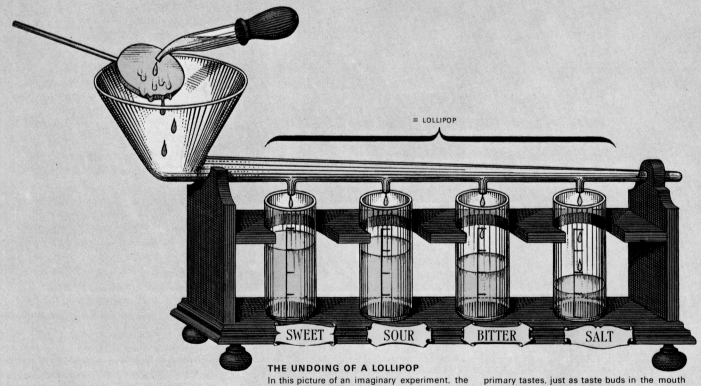

= LOLLIPOP

SWEET   SOUR   BITTER   SALT

THE UNDOING OF A LOLLIPOP
In this picture of an imaginary experiment, the molecules of a lollipop are dissolved by saliva from a medicine dropper. A chemical analysis of the sticky liquid breaks it down into the four primary tastes, just as taste buds in the mouth sort out the components of blends. This lollipop obviously tasted almost as sour as sweet, with a little bitterness and a bit of saltiness.

A girl drinking orange juice tastes acids on the sides of her tongue. She also smells citric aromas and feels the wetness and cold.

Uniting the Senses for Action

Man sees, hear and touches his environment. He also moves skillfully about in it. Virtually every one of his muscular actions, from lifting a forkful of food to the daredevil feats shown on these pages, depends on two vital senses that he seldom thinks about: the sense of balance and the muscle sense. The organs of balance are little fluid-filled structures in the inner ear. Waving in the fluid are hairs which, pulled by movements of the head and by the force of gravity, tell the brain which way the head is moving and which way is up. Thus oriented to the ground, man uses his muscle sense to evaluate messages sent from tiny nerve endings in muscles and joints which tell the brain where each movable part of the body is at any given time. Even the most ordinary actions, such as climbing up stairs, call for a smooth coordination of muscle sense with balance, sight and touch. With training and practice, the brain can learn to coordinate balance, eye and hand with such extraordinary speed that circus performers can walk high wires and juggle six flaming torches.

WALKING A WIRE
The girl in the spotlight does not fall from the tightrope into the clown's eager arms *(left)* because her mind can make extraordinarily delicate interpretations of signals from the organs of balance in her inner ear, and instantly send appropriate orders to her responsive muscles. Her muscle sense keeps her informed of the positions of her arms and legs at every moment.

JUGGLING WITH FIRE
The jugglers *(opposite)* tossing flaming torches to and fro are combining sight, touch, balance and their muscle sense with phenomenal speed. Jugglers learn to flex eye muscles and move limbs far faster than ordinary movements require, but rigorous practice can develop such quickness of eye and sureness of hand that man can play with fire without burning his fingers.

A TELLING MOUTHFUL
The French vintner about to sample one of his wines depends on the acuteness of four of his senses. He judges its color and sniffs its bouquet (odors). Then he swirls it around in his mouth, sucking in air to inhale more aromas, while tasting it for sweetness and acidity. The sense of touch within the mouth informs him of the wine's smoothness and body (density).

A Sharp Sense for Earning a Living

Some of the world's more specialized vocations indicate that man can develop his senses into a phenomenal means for measuring nuances beyond the concern of the average human being. A vintner *(left)* can taste the amounts of alcohol or acidity in a wine to within 1 per cent. Color technicians can see a difference between shades of red indistinguishable to the layman. A baker kneading dough can feel its moisture content within 2 per cent. A piano tuner *(below)* can hear the difference not only between half tones but between quarter tones. Such gifts may be partially inherited, but the evidence is that a normal human with sufficient motive can train taste, smell, hearing, sight or touch to supersensitivity. Refined sensibilities, moreover, work after business hours. The tuner's ear makes him more aware of a singer sliding off key, while the vintner is more likely than the tuner to detect the dash of cinnamon that accidentally fell in the stew.

EIGHTY-EIGHT NOTES FROM ONE
The piano tuner at right need not possess the rare gift of absolute pitch, but he must be able to hear the fine differences in vibration between notes, especially in the high and low registers where most people have difficulty. Using a single tuning fork (middle A) and a wrench, he can tune all 88 notes by comparing their vibrations to that of the fork and to each other.

Life without Sight or Sound

More than half the human race is defective to some degree in one or more of the senses. Touch is distributed over the entire body, but the senses lodged in localized organs, such as the eyes, are prey to accident, disease, aging and genetic malfunction. Human affairs are so involved with the senses that even minor malfunctioning is bothersome: The person with the severe head cold feels cheated that he cannot enjoy his dinner. But taste and smell are probably the least vital senses. More serious is damage to the sense of balance from any of several diseases, including measles, which can cause a terrifying vertigo.

The most cruelly handicapped are the totally deaf or blind. Fortunately, the mind and body make amazing responses when sight or hearing is lost. The deaf learn to read lips, the blind develop acute hearing and touch.

Developments in medical technology promise to revolutionize the lives of the handicapped. In a new area of experimentation, scientists are using sophisticated computers to stimulate electronically the parts of the brain which control vision and hearing. Although these computers cannot confer full functioning of the senses, they may restore partial sight and sound.

A TOUCH OF WOODSMANSHIP
Reaching high to grasp willow branches waving in the breeze, the young man at left, who belongs to a troop of blind Boy Scouts in Pennsylvania, is learning to identify different kinds of trees by the shape and texture of their leaves. He is assisted by Michael J. Kostie, who has worked with this troop for more than 20 years, teaching campcraft and Scouting to blind boys.

FEELING A CONVERSATION
Unable to see or hear, the late Helen Keller *(opposite),* at age 84, is listening to a friend by feeling finger-tappings, which represent letters in the palm-manual alphabet. Her friend—Patty Duke—played the young Helen Keller in the 1959 stage production of *The Miracle Worker,* which dramatized the formidable problems involved in training a blind and deaf child.

8
The Productive Power of Hormones

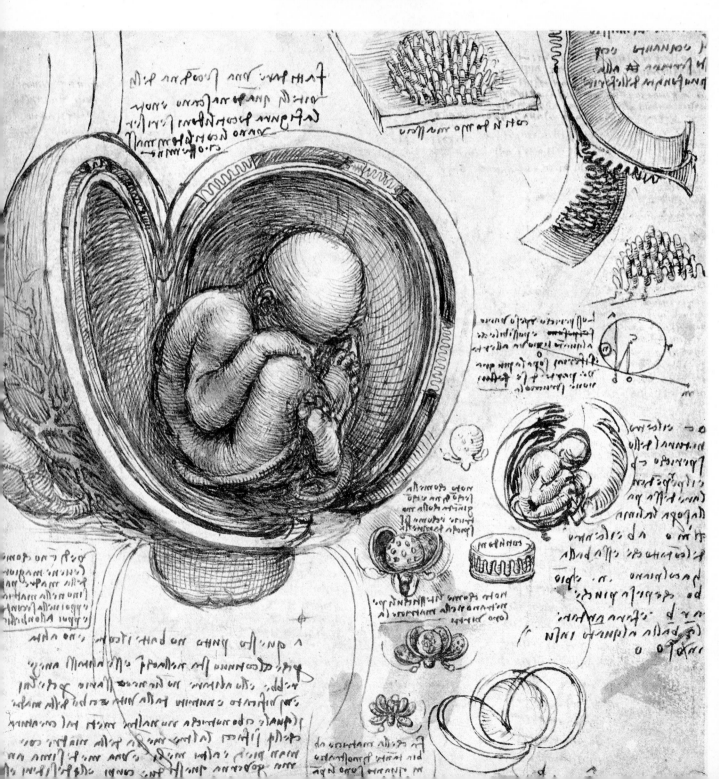

WITH ALL THE CONFIDENCE of armchair diagnosticians, many of us like to equate the state of our health with the state of certain organs of the body which, for want of specifics, we summarily label as glands. Any indisposition not otherwise identifiable is explained away by the assertion that "my glands aren't working right." Unlike other amateur dicta in the field of medicine, this one occasionally proves accurate. Certain glands do, in fact, exert enormous influence over the way we feel and the way we physically react. They wield this power through their control over that intriguing and not yet completely explored province of the body, its internal chemistry.

By definition, a gland is any cell or organ that secretes some substance. Basically, the body contains two different types of glands, which are classified according to the way they secrete. One of these types is the exocrine gland, whose secretions move outward, usually by way of ducts, to some body surface, whether it be the skin itself or, for example, the lining of the digestive or respiratory tract. The second type is the endocrine gland, whose secretions move inward, without benefit of ducts, into the bloodstream.

Among the exocrines are the sweat and sebaceous glands, whose respective secretions of water and oil are clearly visible on the skin; the mucous glands, whose mucus moistens the digestive and respiratory tract; the salivary glands, whose saliva acts as a softener of food upon its entry into the mouth; and the mammary glands, which provide milk for the nursing infant.

The endocrines are the great chemical regulators of bodily function. It is to these glands that the layman unwittingly refers when he blames some sort of glandular mischief as the cause of his ills. The substances which are secreted by the endocrines, and which serve as their chemical messengers, are called hormones, from the Greek word *hormōn*, which means "arouse to activity."

Along with the nervous system, the endocrine system serves as the major means of controlling the activities of the body. The nervous system is, so to speak, built for speed; it enables the body to adjust its internal processes rapidly, as changes are occurring in the environment. The endocrines, on the other hand, regulate continuing processes which have longer duration, including the body's growth, its sexual maturation and its ability to reproduce.

Only within the past century has any real understanding of the endocrine glands been achieved. Even today we are not certain how many there are. Some are well known: the pituitary at the base of the brain; the thyroid gland in the neck; the four parathyroids lying behind the thyroid; the adrenals, perched atop the kidneys like miniature peaked caps; the insulin-making Islets of Langerhans in the pancreas; the

ON THE BRINK OF BIRTH
A full-term fetus, nearing birth, is shown in its mother's womb in this Leonardo da Vinci drawing, one of the first accurate renderings of a part of the human anatomy. The smaller sketches depict details of the uterus. Of all the triumphs of the body, its crowning glory is the power to reproduce its kind and pass some of its hereditary characteristics on to later generations.

ovaries in the abdomen of the female; the testicles in the scrotum of the male. The placenta, which feeds the unborn child, also behaves like an endocrine, manufacturing special chemicals essential to a successful pregnancy.

Recent studies have confirmed that the brain itself acts as an endocrine, since it, too, produces hormones. In fact, one part of the brain, the hypothalamus, is attached by both nerves and blood vessels to the pituitary gland. The hypothalamus secretes many hormones that regulate the release of the pituitary hormones; it is also a nervous center that controls the release of adrenalin from the adrenal gland. Both parts of the hypothalamus act together to keep the body in chemical balance.

A troop of little giants

Compared to such organs as the heart or the lungs, the endocrines seem to be ridiculously small and unimpressive. They are bits of tissue tucked away in obscure corners of the body; all of them together weigh no more than about five ounces. They make minute amounts of hormones that are rapidly circulated to all parts of the body. Nonetheless, in the widespread control which they exercise over the body, they are little giants. The key to their extraordinary power lies in the hormones they secrete— which include among them some of the most powerful and remarkable substances in the body.

All hormones regulate one or more chemical reactions in the body, but they seem to work in many different ways. One hormone may alter cell membranes so that it is possible for glucose from the blood to enter the cells more freely. Another may change the spatial relationship of enzymes, the chemical catalysts resident in the cells, in order to speed up metabolic reactions. Still others may stimulate the production of other necessary chemicals within the cells. The precise mechanism of action of each hormone has not been completely identified, but many new facts are discovered each year.

A most important technical advance, which has made possible many of these discoveries, is called the radioimmunoassay method of measuring minute amounts of hormones in blood and tissue. This new laboratory technique has resulted in a radically new understanding of how hormones change cell functions. It seems that the hormone molecule acts like a key and fits into special locks that exist on cell membranes. Each tissue has its own kind of lock, so a particular hormone, like estrogen, may influence the metabolism of cells in the breast but have little effect on the cells of the eye. The locks on the cell membranes are called hormone receptors. Once the hormone key enters the appropriate receptor lock, it opens a chemical pathway inside the cell which leads to metabolic changes. The chemical pathway which seems to be most commonly used in many hormone-

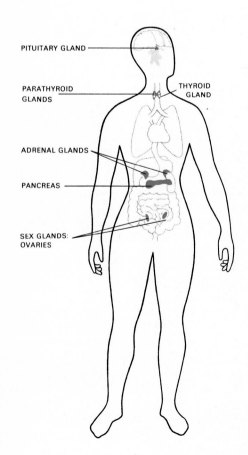

PITUITARY GLAND

PARATHYROID
GLANDS

THYROID
GLAND

ADRENAL GLANDS

PANCREAS

SEX GLANDS:
OVARIES

THE ENDOCRINE GLANDS
Endocrine glands regulate many vital body processes. The thyroid helps control energy production; the parathyroid distributes calcium between blood and bone. Adrenal glands regulate salt and water levels and secrete stimulants; cells in the pancreas control blood sugar. Sex glands govern reproduction and secondary sexual characteristics. The pituitary controls some of the other endocrine glands.

mediated reactions involves an enzyme called Cyclic AMP. This enzyme is often referred to as the "second messenger" of the hormones. Whatever the specific steps prove to be, one thing is clear: hormonal activity must remain in delicate balance—like salt in the stew—or the entire body will be thrown out of kilter.

The endocrine gland most familiar to the layman is the thyroid. Located at the base of the neck just below the Adam's apple, this gland can be felt from the outside, and can thus be examined by the doctor more readily than any other; an enlargement or swelling of the thyroid may be apparent even by casual observation across a room. The hormones produced by the thyroid—iodine-protein compounds called thyroxine and tri-iodothyronine—exercise control over the rate at which food is converted into heat and energy in all the body's cells.

Without sufficient thyroid hormones the individual feels constantly cold, drowsy and unable to accomplish anything without exerting considerable effort. His respiration is slow, his heart rate is sluggish, his appetite and sex functioning are both below par; sometimes he will gain weight in spite of a distinctly meager diet. The opposite of this torpid syndrome of hypothyroidism is hyperthyroidism, produced by an excess of thyroid hormones. An individual with this condition will probably have a tendency to be nervous, jittery and overactive, with a pounding heart and labored respirations, able to gorge and yet still lose weight, as though all the body fires were burning out of control. Most thyroid-deficiency diseases are caused either by a lack of iodine in the diet or by a curious immune response in which individuals develop antibodies that attack and destroy their own thyroid glands. Next to diabetes, thyroid diseases are the most common endocrine ailments.

The harvest of hidden islands

In sharp contrast to the easily approachable thyroid are the best hidden of all the endocrine glands: the tiny islands of insulin-producing cells scattered throughout the pancreas. Estimates of their number range from 250,000 to 2.5 million. A German anatomist, Paul Langerhans, first noticed them in 1869, and they are known as the Islets of Langerhans in his honor. Each of these minute clumps of cells acts as a diminutive endocrine; together they make up, as it were, an organ within an organ, busily manufacturing their hormones and generally disregarding the pancreatic cells all around them, as though they were located in some completely different part of the body.

Langerhans did not, in fact, recognize what he was seeing when he observed these separate clusters of cells during microscopic examinations of pancreatic tissue. But nine years later a French physician, Etienne Lancereaux, detected a relationship between the pancreas and an age-old disease

ENDOCRINES AND GROWTH
Charles Stratton ("Tom Thumb") and his bride, Lavinia Warren, were intelligent, well-proportioned dwarfs less than three feet tall. Their stunted growth was probably caused by an insufficiency of pituitary hormones that may result in a childish but normally proportioned figure and normal intelligence. In recent years, pituitary dwarfism has become more rare as hormone-deficient children are treated with somatotropin, also known as human growth hormone.

characterized by great hunger and thirst, wasting away of the body and ultimate death in coma. The ancients called the disease "diabetes," after a Greek word meaning "siphon," because it was marked by the passage of excessive quantities of urine. Later the word "mellitus" (meaning "honey-sweet") was added to the name because of the quantity of sugar found in the urine of diabetics.

By the end of the 19th Century, medical scientists, following Lancereaux's lead, confirmed the fact that diabetes mellitus resulted when the pancreas did not function properly, causing one of the body's main fuels—the simple sugar glucose—to be passed out of the body in urine. But they could not ascertain the substance in the pancreas which facilitated the efficient use of glucose.

Today we know that hormones manufactured in the Islets of Langerhans—insulin and the more recently discovered glucagon and somatostatin—help to regulate the amount of sugar which is available at any given time for the cells to use for the production of heat and energy. Insulin acts by fitting the receptor locks on muscle and fat cells, opening an avenue for glucose entry.

When the pancreas does not make enough insulin, or makes it too slowly, the blood sugar goes up because muscle and fat cells cease to take up the glucose normally. In addition, some scientists believe that when a person with a hereditary disposition to diabetes puts on too much weight, the fat-cell membranes are stretched and the insulin locks become distorted. Often, if such a patient merely loses the excess weight, the blood sugar drops back to a normal level.

Insulin from bacteria

Until recently, all diabetics who required insulin were given doses which were derived from cattle and pigs. But allergic reactions to these foreign substances can result, and it is possible that supplies might run short in the future. In the exciting new field of genetic engineering, doctors are discovering that large quantities of human insulin can be synthesized, by restructuring the cells of the common *Escherichia coli* bacteria (which ordinarily do not produce insulin), thereby ensuring a constant supply for diabetics.

Hormones of an equally vital if vastly different nature are produced by the adrenal glands. Each adrenal is, in fact, two endocrine glands in one, and each secretes its own completely separate class of hormones. One type is manufactured in the central part of each adrenal, the adrenal medulla. Another type is manufactured in the outer shell of the gland, the adrenal cortex.

The hormones made in the adrenal medulla are epinephrine and norepinephrine. Both play a part in helping the body respond to emergency situa-

THE DUAL ROLE OF THE PANCREAS
The pancreas, shown below in successively increased magnifications, is located below and behind the stomach. It secretes a digestive juice by way of a duct into the small intestine, but it also contains clusters of special cells—endocrine cells within a digestive organ—called the Islets of Langerhans. Two types of cells in the clusters, alpha and beta, pour their secretions directly into the blood. Alpha cells produce a hormone called glucagon, beta cells produce insulin; both help regulate blood sugar.

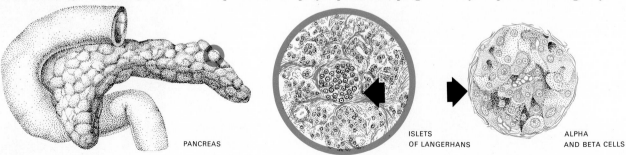

PANCREAS

ISLETS OF LANGERHANS

ALPHA AND BETA CELLS

tions. Epinephrine, more popularly known as adrenalin from the days when it was thought to be the only hormone made by the adrenals, is a powerful stimulant with effects throughout the body. In times of stress—when we become excited, frightened or angry—epinephrine can speed up respiration, raise the blood pressure, sharpen the reflexes and put the body on guard to fight or flee. Whatever the emotion involved, we experience the same chemical reaction as a result of the epinephrine poured out into the bloodstream by the adrenals. Norepinephrine serves as an effective aide-de-camp to epinephrine at such times, causing an increase in the amount of blood flowing through the heart and constricting the skin capillaries so that blood is forced out of them and shunted, by the action of the epinephrine, to the body's major organs. The nervous system also makes adrenalin-like compounds that act together with the adrenalin from the adrenal medulla to help maintain body functions during periods of stress or excitement.

Cortisone and company

The hormones manufactured in the adrenal cortex are comparatively recent discoveries; like insulin, they were found in the course of the study of a disease, in this instance a rare one—Addison's disease. This condition, named for Thomas Addison, who first described it in 1855, is marked by muscular weakness, a peculiar bronzing of the skin, generalized apathy and collapse. Many victims of Addison's disease were found to have adrenal glands damaged by tuberculosis.

Intensive research into the adrenals followed. In 1929 two biochemists, working on experiments with dogs, isolated the first known hormonal compound of the adrenal cortex. By 1938 Dr. Edward Kendall of the Mayo Clinic and his co-workers had isolated no less than six different hormonal compounds which are made by the adrenal cortex, among them the now celebrated cortisone.

These hormones, unlike insulin or thyroxine, are not protein compounds, but substances which the biochemists labeled steroids, after a Greek word meaning "solid," or "firm." Because these particular hormones are manufactured by the adrenal cortex they are called "adrenocortico-steroids," or "corticoids" for short. Since Kendall's first pioneering experiments, no less than 28 compounds, all of the same steroid family, have been found in the adrenal cortex.

The steroid hormones were soon shown to play a far greater role in the body than was first suspected. They help the kidneys regulate the critical balance of the salt and water content of body fluids inside and outside the cells. They also influence the body's ability to build up and break down proteins, to form antibodies against bacteria and viruses, to repair damaged tissue, and to control inflammation. Indeed, because of their ability

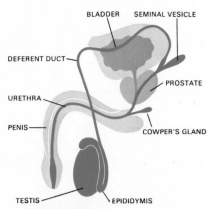

A SEED IS BORN
The male reproductive system *(above)* manufactures and transports the tiny sperm cells of human seeds. Formed in the testes in astronomical numbers, sperm cells are stored in the epididymis and travel, suspended in secretions from the seminal vesicle, prostate and Cowper's gland, along the deferent duct into the urethra that leads through the penis.

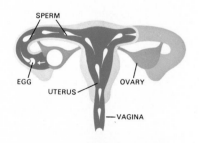

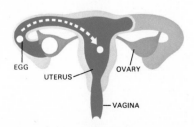

LIFE: ONE SEED + ONE EGG
Life begins when an egg, previously released from one of the two ovaries *(upper diagram)*, merges with just one of the hundreds of millions of sperm cells supplied through the vagina by the male reproductive system. The fertilized egg then descends to the wall of the uterus *(lower diagram)*, where it implants itself to begin gestation *(opposite)*.

to suppress inflammation of joints and to reduce scarring of inflamed joint capsules, these hormones sometimes work almost miraculously to relieve pain and reduce inflammation. Corticoids also reduce inflammation in nephrosis and rheumatic fever, speed the healing of skin wounds, and help in the treatment of gout.

A bonanza in beef cattle

Originally the steroids could be obtained only with great difficulty: one early researcher had to grind up a ton of the adrenal glands of beef cattle in order to secure less than a half ounce of one particular hormonal compound. But since that time a succession of steroids has been synthesized in the laboratory.

While in most cases the hormones which are manufactured by one endocrine gland differ considerably from those which are made by other endocrine glands, the adrenal cortical hormones are structurally very similar to those secreted by the sex glands—the female ovaries and the male testes. These hormones—testosterone and androsterone in the male, estrogen and progesterone in the female—are actually produced in both sexes. But the male sex hormones normally predominate in men, the female sex hormones in women.

During childhood, production of sex hormones is very low. As the male approaches sexual maturity, however, the testes begin secreting more and more of the male hormones. These substances effect striking growth changes such as the development of beard and muscles, the enlargement of the larynx (with a resulting deepening of the voice), the maturation of sex organs and the development of sexual urges. They are also believed to stimulate sperm production in the testicles.

The female sex hormones bring about the development of the hips and breasts, and the other so-called secondary sex characteristics that differentiate woman from man. They also act to prepare the uterus to receive and to sustain a fertilized ovum. In fact, the cycle of menstruation experienced by all sexually mature females is a direct consequence of the waxing and waning of hormones on a more or less regular monthly schedule until menopause—another result of hormonal change—occurs.

The hormonal compounds called prostaglandins, which are manufactured in many cells in the body, are particularly active in the uterus. It has been found that these compounds can cause strong uterine contractions at the end of the menstrual cycle—similar to but much less severe in pain than the contractions that attend birth. The typical cramping experienced during these times may be the result of a large release of prostaglandins by the uterine cells.

Only in recent times has science found ways to increase or decrease fertility by means of hormones. Probably the most important social impact has come from the contraceptive pills, which have enabled millions of women to regulate when and how often they ovulate. The pills contain compounds that are chemically like the ovarian hormones, estrogen and progesterone, but in concentrations higher than the ovary produces during a normal menstrual cycle.

The foreign steroids get into the bloodstream and are carried to the pituitary gland, where they act to inhibit the release of luteinizing hormone, or LH, which is essential for the formation of the corpus luteum, the mass of endocrine tissue embedded within the ovaries that controls periodic ovulation. Without an adequate LH level, a woman does not produce an egg in mid-cycle and therefore cannot conceive. Unfortunately, these ovarian hormone substitutes, while acting to suppress fertility, can have other effects which may be harmful. For example, in a small percentage of susceptible women, they may lead to the formation of blood clots, while in others they may increase the chances of developing uterine cancer or heart attacks.

In spite of the fact that hormones have widely different functions and are produced in widely different parts of the body, they do not go their merry way independent of any regulation at all. Some higher form of control is required to determine, for example, when more thyroid hormone is needed and when production should slow down, when adrenal cortical hormones are needed and when not. The gland which fulfills this master role is the pituitary, one of the tiniest endocrines of all. It controls the hormonal output not only of the thyroid gland and adrenal cortex, but also of the sex glands.

A little gland with a big punch

The pituitary hangs from the bottom of the brain by a little stalk just above the nasal passage. Vesalius, who named it, mistakenly believed that it discharged mucus into the nose, and therefore he derived the name from the Latin word for "nasal secretion." The pituitary is insignificant in appearance—about the size of an acorn—but it packs an extremely powerful punch. Like the adrenals, the pituitary is actually two glands in one—posterior and anterior. Of the two, the posterior pituitary manufactures no hormones of its own, but stores and secretes two that are initially produced in the hypothalamus. These hormones are oxytocin, believed to stimulate labor at the end of pregnancy, and vasopressin, which helps the body retain its fluids. The anterior part of the pituitary, however, is what gives this potent endocrine gland its major claim to sovereignty. One hormone secreted in the anterior pituitary controls the over-all growth of the body. Five more have the task of spurring hormone production in other endocrine glands.

The growth hormone somatotropin regulates the growth of the bone,

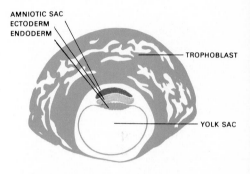

A 12-DAY-OLD EMBRYO
Every hour of the human gestation period proceeds on a rigid schedule. By the 12th day, the embryo has become two vitally different cell layers: the endoderm, forming the roof of a vestigial yolk sac, and the ectoderm, at the base of the undeveloped amniotic sac. The trophoblast is a surrounding mass of cells which nourish the embryo.

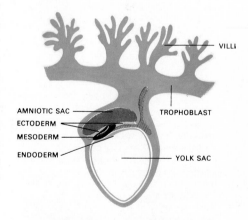

PROGRESS ON THE 15TH DAY
Cell differentiation continues, and the mesoderm develops from the ectoderm. The ectoderm will form outer tissues and the nervous system; the mesoderm blood vessels, muscle, bone and many organs; the endoderm interior linings. The trophoblast and its villi, which absorb nourishment from the uterine wall, will become the placenta.

muscle and other tissues from top to toe. In some individuals, fortunately only a few, underproduction or overproduction of somatotropin occurs during childhood. Either extreme causes growth abnormalities. Overproduction results in gigantism. Underproduction results in dwarfism; the pituitary dwarf almost never attains adult proportions or sexual maturity, although his intelligence is normal. Somatotropin, like insulin, is now being synthesized by genetic engineers and may come to offer a relatively inexpensive form of treatment for children who are suffering from pituitary dwarfism.

Most of us, happily, need have little concern with somatotropin, since its aberrations are the exception. Of considerably greater urgency for the average person are the anterior pituitary hormones, which regulate other endocrines. One of these, the thyroid-stimulating hormone, TSH, signals the thyroid to manufacture thyroxine when the level gets too low. The adrenocorticotrophic hormone, ACTH, stimulates production of the steroid hormones by the adrenal cortex.

Three other anterior pituitary hormones are vital to sex functioning. The follicle-stimulating hormone, FSH, stimulates the testes to produce sperm and the ovaries to secrete estrogen. The luteinizing hormone, LH, spurs hormone production in the sex glands of both men and women. Production of the female sex hormone progesterone, in particular, is abetted by the lactogenic hormone, prolactin, which also stimulates the mammary glands to produce milk.

A feedback control system

Endocrine control works both ways. Just as a thermostat, which fires a furnace into activity when the temperature in the room has dropped, is itself turned off when the temperature rises high enough, the production of each of the stimulating hormones in the pituitary is suppressed by the presence in the blood of the hormone which it stimulated. Thus, as the level of thyroxine drops, TSH is poured out to goad the thyroid cells into activity; but as soon as production has been speeded up, the very presence of thyroid hormone in quantity in the bloodstream blocks the pituitary's release of more TSH until the activity of the thyroid slows down once more. The result of this cycle is the maintenance of a remarkably steady balance of thyroid hormone in the bloodstream at all times. Such a feedback system serves to regulate levels of adrenal hormones and sex hormones in much the same way.

All of the unfolding intricacies of the body's chemical regulators and nervous system, and indeed all of the discoveries which man has made about the structure and function of his body, would seem to be pointless were it not for the fact that the death of an individual does not necessarily bring to an end the contribution he or she makes to the human species. Like

THE GROWTH OF AN EMBRYO
During the first 12 weeks of pregnancy, the embryo develops from a single cell into a recognizable human being. In the uterus, the embryo is cushioned against shock by the soft uterine wall and wrapped in the fluid-filled amniotic sac. In the first illustration, the embryo is about a fifth of an inch long. The vestigial yolk sac, almost useless in the gestation of man, is relatively large. By the fifth week, buds for arms and legs are advanced, the mouth is forming and eyes appear. Sex organs form as ridges on the kidneys. By the sixth week, fingers are forming and the mouth begins to draw into shape; the embryo's tail has been all but absorbed. By the 12th week, the small being is called a fetus, and has such human characteristics as a well-established nose, lips, cheeks, eyelids and ears.

176

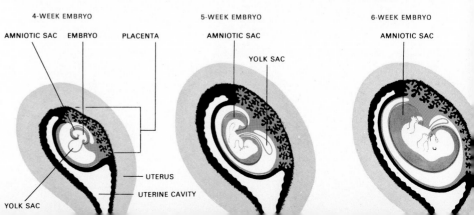

most other living organisms, the human body has one capability that gives it a certain claim to physical immortality: the ability to reproduce itself, to pass part of its body substance directly along to future generations. Certain of the cells of the body—the male sperm and the female ovum, or egg—are the seeds from which new and unique individual members of the species can grow.

For the first 36 hours after the egg is fertilized by the sperm it seems simply to rest, as if gathering strength for the difficult job ahead. Then it begins to divide rapidly into new cells. For several days the new cells appear precisely the same as the old, forming a round blob of tissue shaped like a hollow ball—the embryo. But then a few of the cells begin to vary from the others. The embryo dents in upon itself to form a tiny cuplike structure; the cup stretches out to become an elongated pouch. The cells which line the inside of the pouch begin to look taller and thinner than those on the outside.

By the 12th day after conception, two distinct layers of cells—the inner and the outer—have formed. Next, a third layer of cells begins to appear between these two. By the middle of the third week the original ovum has produced three quite separate layers which are known as the precursor cells—the ectoderm, or outer layer; the endoderm, or inner layer; and the mesoderm, or middle layer. Soon these begin to form the organs of a rudimentary human body.

Soon after they appear, the precursor cells differentiate. The endoderm elongates to become a primitive gut, which then forms pockets, or buds, that develop into tiny air tubes, lungs, liver and digestive organs. The ectoderm forms a crease along the back of the embryo which later differentiates into the nervous tissue of the spinal cord and brain; other parts of the ectoderm form the skin, hair, nails and sensory organs. From the mesoderm, bone and muscle and connective tissue begin to emerge; so do the kidneys and the blood vessels.

Auguries of a masterwork

By the end of three months the fetus—even though it is still no more than three inches in length—has developed virtually every detail of its basic structure. The remaining six months are devoted almost exclusively to the growth and refinement of this new body. Fingerprints appear; lung tissue is perfected for later use in breathing; muscles grow and are exercised (which accounts for the lusty kicking which the pregnant woman frequently feels). When the baby is finally born we see a completely finished, loudly squalling human being with each of its many parts working perfectly—all arisen from a single living cell which has proliferated almost beyond belief.

The marvelous mechanism for reproducing the species assures us that

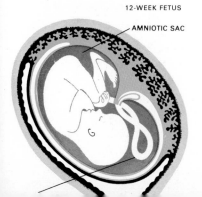

12-WEEK FETUS

AMNIOTIC SAC

these bodies of ours, with their complex structure and function, serve a continuing purpose. It also presents us with an inescapable fact: it is nature, not man, that has devised this most amazing, delicate, powerful organism ever to appear on earth. Science continues in its striving to exert some control over the forces of nature. The birth in England in 1978 of Louise Brown, the first test-tube baby, is just one example of the recent advances which have been made in governing the beginning of life itself. Yet the most brilliant and imaginative researchers know—or soon learn—that nature must be with them and not against them if their work is ultimately to succeed.

Above all, those who study the human body feel increasing wonder at this remarkable organism and its capabilities the more they learn about it. No man-made devices are ever likely to rival it either in complexity or efficiency.

Dr. Charles Bradford, a distinguished Boston orthopedist, summed up the feelings that must regularly inspire those entrusted with the body's care: "The doctor observes the anatomical perfection of the hand, and the stabilizing microphones of the ear, and the television screens of the retina, and the multiple batteries of electronic computers in the brain, and from all these he gains a new reverence for the incomprehensible power that created man, so anxiously and so wonderfully wrought."

The Beginnings of Human Life

More than a century ago, the English poet Samuel Taylor Coleridge wrote: "The history of man for nine months preceding his birth would, probably, be far more interesting, and contain events of greater moment, than all the threescore and ten years that follow it." Until recent times, the 38-week span between conception and birth, during which a single fertilized egg is transformed into a vastly complex, self-sufficient organism, constituted the most eventful and least understood period of time in human life. But newly developed tools and techniques have enabled medical researchers to trace—and even to photograph—every step of the remarkable reproductive process. Their findings have shed new light not only on the phenomenon of conception, but also on the causes of the defects that each year terminate more than a half-million pregnancies in the United States alone, and which handicap another quarter million of the 3.5 million survivors.

A TRILLION-CELLED ORGANISM
A healthy baby boy represents the successful conclusion of a process that began when one of his mother's 400 eggs was fertilized by one of his father's several hundred million spermatazoa. At birth his body was made up of trillions of cells, including some 10 billion in his brain—a structure so unique that the odds against duplication by the same parents are about 144 billion to one.

A SWOLLEN FOLLICLE

The ovulation process, seen in this remarkable sequence of photographs by German gynecologist Hans Frangenheim, begins with the appearance on the ovary surface of a Graafian follicle, a fluid-filled swelling that contains a single ovum *(dark spot)*, surrounded by nurturing cells.

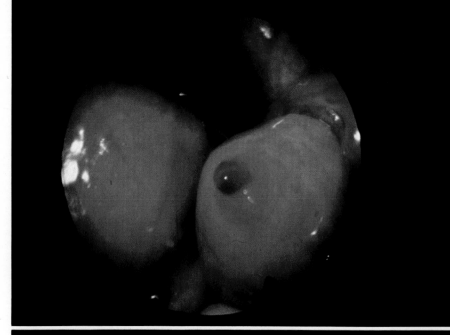

AN EMERGING EGG

As the follicle strains against the thin outer wall of the ovary, the ovum can be seen protruding from the top of the follicle. The wall is about to rupture with the force of a miniature volcano, spewing the follicle contents—cells, fluid and ovum—into the abdominal cavity.

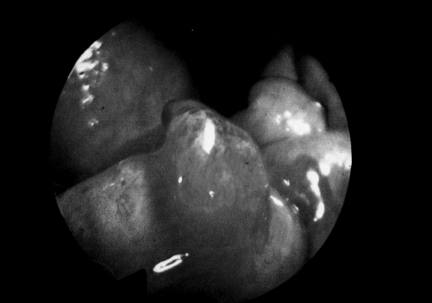

A JOURNEY COMMENCES

The dark ovum drifts free in the narrow gap of about an inch (2.5 cm) between the ruptured ovary *(right)* and the unseen fimbriae that draw the ovum into the Fallopian tube. Occasionally an ovum misses the opening and floats aimlessly, making fertilization virtually impossible.

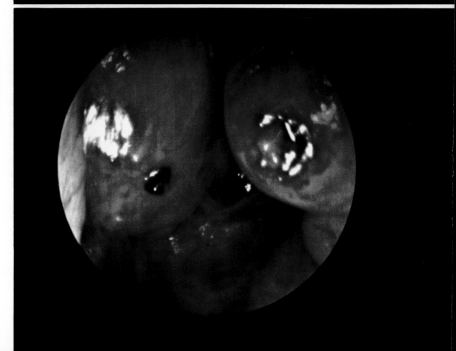

The Fateful Voyage of a Solitary Cell

The single female cell from which the body is formed is the egg, or ovum, a microscopic bit of protoplasm about $\frac{1}{175}$ inch (0.15 mm) in diameter and weighing about one twenty millionth of an ounce (0.000014 g). About once every four weeks, an egg bursts from one of the two ovaries in a process like the one shown opposite, photographed by a laparoscopic technique that illuminates the abdominal region with a light-transmitting glass probe.

The free-floating egg is soon drawn into the nearby tulip-shaped opening of the Fallopian tube by the undulant motions of the fimbriae, fingerlike projections of the tube. Once inside, the egg is prodded on a slow journey of about six inches (15 cm) to the uterus by ciliary action and muscular contraction. It is during the first third of this journey that the egg must be fertilized by sperm swarming in from the opposite direction. When this occurs, the fertilized egg eventually implants itself in the uterine wall and begins to form an embryo. If the egg is not fertilized—as is the case with most of the 400 or so eggs released during a woman's lifetime—it is expelled from the uterus during menstruation. If the maximum number of eggs were fertilized, a woman might find herself the mother of 30 children.

THE EGG'S PROGRESS

Drawn into the Fallopian tube by the undulating fimbriae, an ovum begins its three-day journey from ovary to uterus. Fertilization usually takes place within the first 12 hours. The ovum then divides itself into smaller and smaller cells, all identical in genetic make-up to the original. About eight days later, this mass of cells, now called an embryo, implants itself in the uterus.

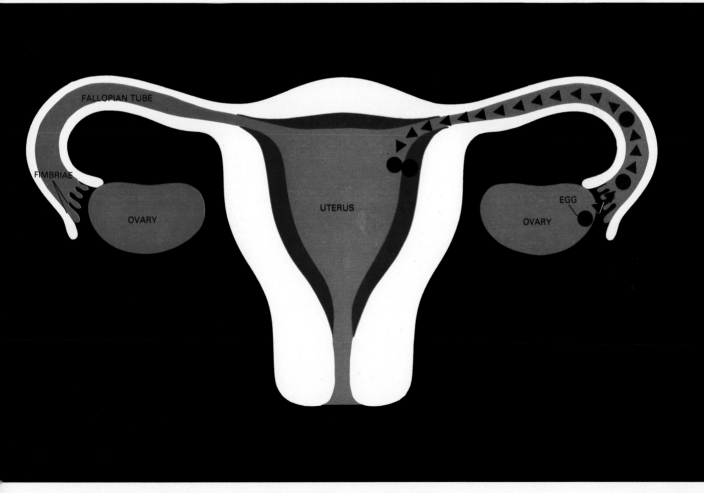

FALLOPIAN TUBE

FIMBRIAE

OVARY

UTERUS

EGG

OVARY

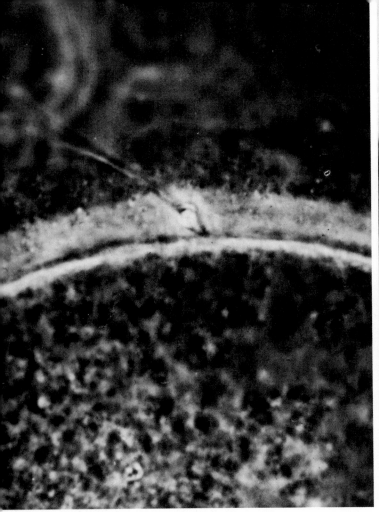

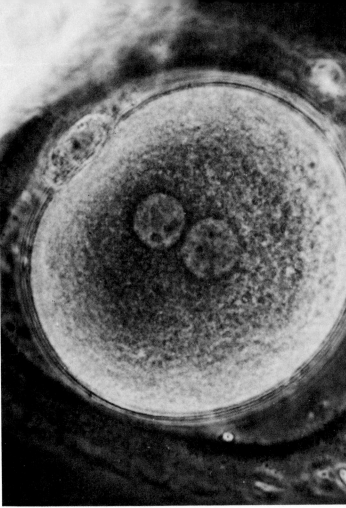

Fertilization takes place as one of a multitude of spermatozoa penetrates the egg's transparent membrane, the zona pellucida.

The male and female genetic units, called pronuclei, approach before merging to become the nucleus of a new living cell.

The original cell cleaves itself into four cells *(left)* within two days, and then doubles again to eight cells *(right)* a few hours later.

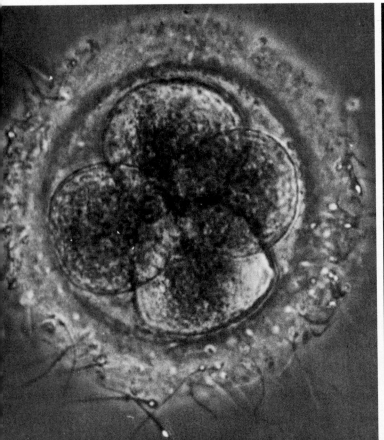

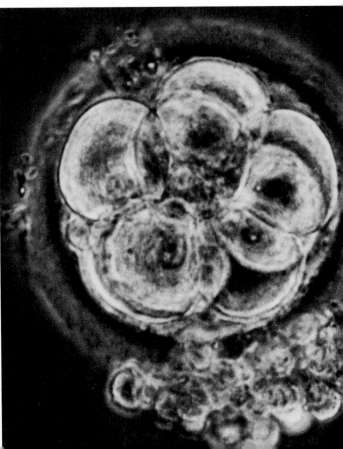

The First Signs of Life

In 1963 biologist Margaret Shea Gilbert wrote: "Life begins for each of us at an unfelt, unknown, and unhonored instant when a minute wriggling sperm plunges headlong into a mature ovum."

In the years since, that mysterious instant has been observed and photographed by scientists studying the rapid and complex changes which accompany fertilization. It is not necessary for them to probe the confines of the Fallopian tubes. In these fascinating laboratory photographs, provided by English scientists Patrick Steptoe and Robert Edwards, an egg extracted from an ovary is shown over a period of four days, from the moment of fertilization to the formation of a multicelled blastocyst, the last stage before embryo formation. Steptoe made medical history in 1977 by successfully reinserting a laboratory-fertilized egg into the uterus of its donor, who later gave birth to a normal child.

Natural fertilization ordinarily occurs within hours after the egg enters the Fallopian tube. Buffeted by a swarm of sperm moving through the tube from the opposite direction, the egg is penetrated by a single spermatozoon and instantly becomes impermeable to the other sperm, which will eventually scatter and then die.

In the fertilized egg, a remarkable series of events begins. Within 12 hours the spermatozoon, shorn of cap and tail but retaining its 23 chromosomes from the father, merges with an egg nucleus containing 23 chromosomes from the mother. About 36 hours later the new nucleus divides in half. Cleavage continues at a more rapid rate as the egg divides into four, eight and 16 cells. When it enters the uterus, about a week after fertilization, the egg possesses 64 to 128 cells and is almost a rudimentary embryo.

e egg becomes a morula of 16 to 32 cells *(left)* in three days, and a hollow-centered blastocyst of 64 to 128 cells *(right)* in four days.

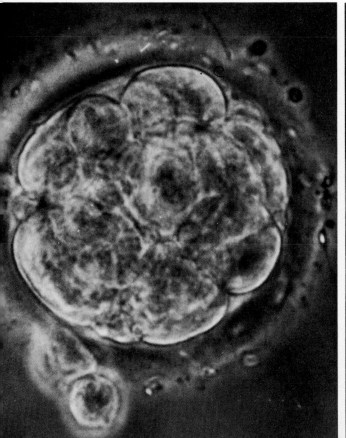 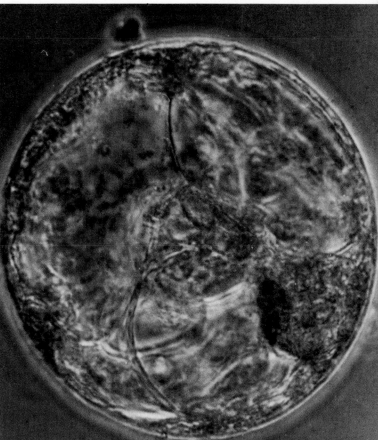

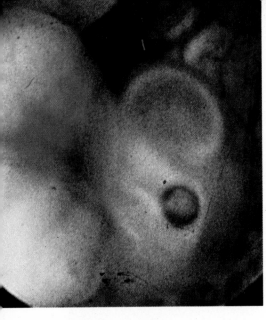

A FETUS AT 7 WEEKS
A living fetus, less than an inch (2.5 cm) long and looking more like a mouse than a human, is photographed during a fetoscopic examination. The heart, visible as a reddish mass, is already beating and a primitive eye is facing toward the side of a large but undefined head.

A FETUS AT 16 WEEKS
A well-formed leg dominates this fetoscopic view of a four-month-old fetus crammed into its amniotic sac. At this stage the fetus is about 6 inches (15.2 cm) long and weighs less than a quarter of a pound (113 g). The body and organs are complete, and the skeleton is now forming.

The Shaping of a Tiny Body

In its first month, the embryo is barely recognizable as human. Though it has the beginnings of a brain, heart, nervous system and eyes, it also has rudimentary gills and a tail.

But in the second month, the embryo starts to become the distinctively human fetus seen in the photographs, taken in the uterus with a technique known as fetoscopy. Gills and tail all but disappear, eyes begin to move to the front, and fingers and toes appear on clublike arms and legs. By the end of three months—the first trimester—organs, muscles and nerves begin to interact and the fetus kicks, flexes and squirms.

The second trimester is one of rapid growth, during which the fetus triples in size and weight. Trunk and limbs stretch to form the greater part of a body that was once half head. Organs are almost fully formed and the heart beats 120 to 160 times a minute. By the end of six months the fetus is about 13 inches (30 cm) long and weighs about 1½ pounds (0.7 kg).

In the last trimester the fetus adds about 7 inches (18 cm) in length and 5 pounds (2.25 kg) in weight, filling the uterus so snugly that movement is somewhat restricted. By the time the fetus assumes the upside-down birth position, it has taken on the rounded shape of the baby it is to become.

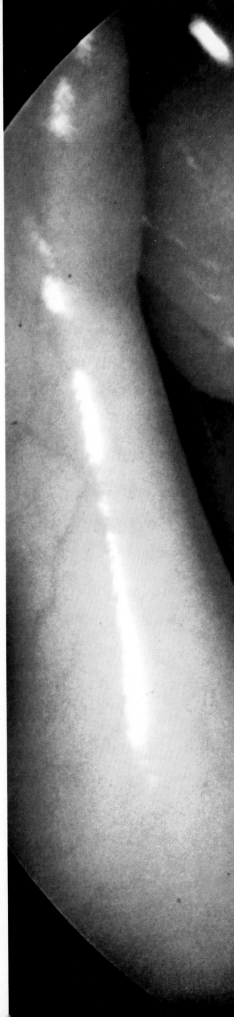

A JUMBLE OF FAMILIAR FORMS
Another view of a 16-week-old fetus reveals the limbs, face and genitals of a fully formed boy. The body is immersed in amniotic fluid within its clear protective sac. The hand is poised over the tubular umbilical cord that provides nourishment to the fetus from the mother's placenta.

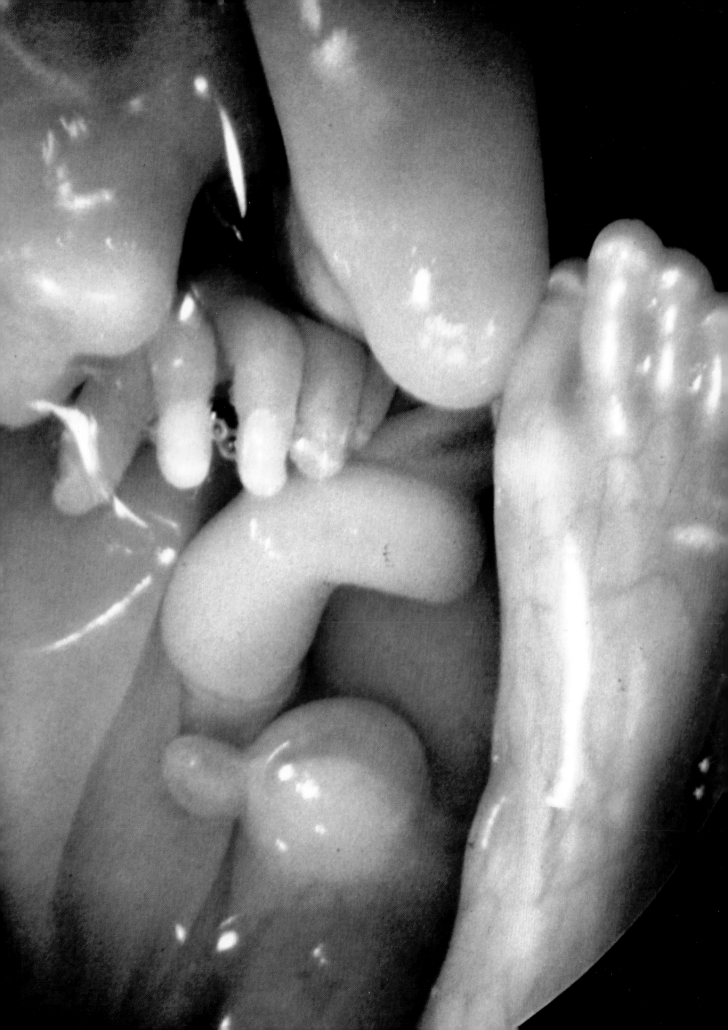

Guarding the Health of an Unborn Child

The birth of a child is hardly routine. In the United States, one out of every seven pregnancies is unsuccessful and one in every 14 live births reveals a birth defect, from astigmatism to Down's syndrome (mongolism).

In an attempt to reduce these tolls, scientists are developing sophisticated techniques to detect disease, immaturity and distress in fetuses. The most effective of these techniques is amniocentesis, the removal from the amniotic sac of a small quantity of flu-id which can be tested to detect the presence of some 80 metabolic diseases as well as such chromosomal abnormalities as Down's syndrome.

Another technique, the electronic monitoring of the fetal heartbeat, is routinely used on two thirds of all pregnant women during the last days and weeks before they deliver. The recorded heartbeat pattern may reveal distress signals which are urgent enough to call for emergency delivery of the baby by Caesarean section.

A TELLING FLUID
Performing amniocentesis on a pregnant woman, a doctor extracts amniotic fluid with a long-needled syringe. Analysis of the fluid, and the castoff fetal cells it contains, reveals the sex, health and chromosome make-up of fetuses as young as 16 weeks. The test is often given to women over 35, whose babies run a greater risk of birth defects than those of younger women.

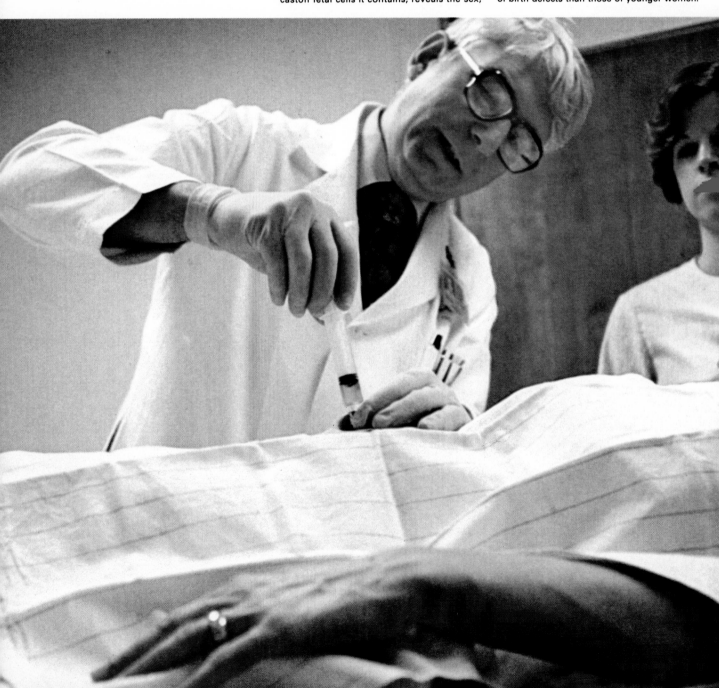

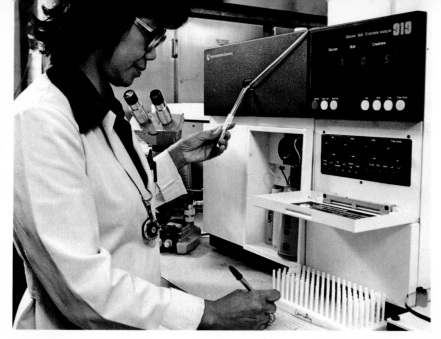

DIAGNOSIS BY MACHINE
An electronic analyzer sucks up a sample of amniotic fluid proffered by a laboratory technician and flashes red digits to indicate levels of glucose, blood-urea nitrogen or creatinine.

AN ELECTRONIC STETHOSCOPE
While an expectant mother rests in Washington's Columbia Hospital for Women, two electrodes strapped to her abdomen continuously record her contractions and the heartbeat of the fetus. Digits on the machine reveal the characteristic leaps and drops of the fetal heart rate.

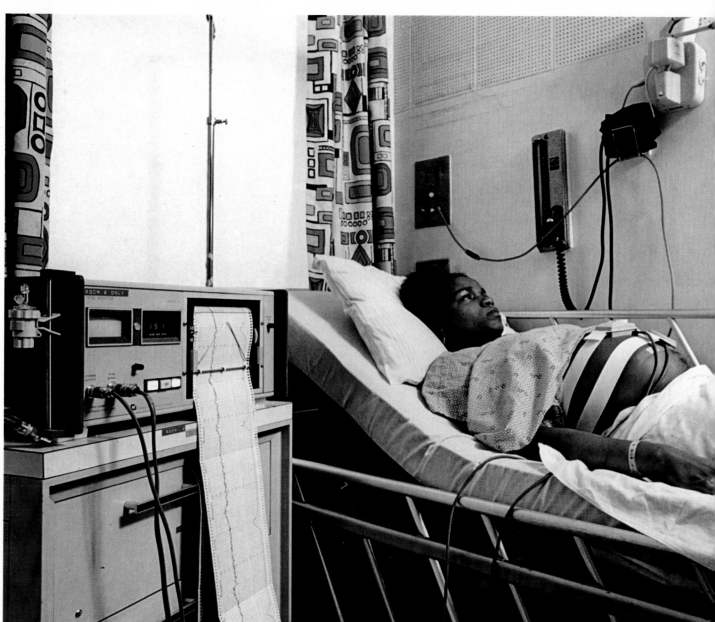

Probing with Ultrasound

The most dramatic of the monitoring techniques used to observe the progress of fetal development is echosonography—the use of high ultrasonic frequencies to provide images, called sonograms, like the one opposite. By beaming ultrasonic pulses into the abdomen of a pregnant woman and studying the sonograms that are electronically assembled by the returning echoes, doctors can "see" the fetus without risking techniques involving X-rays or fetoscopes.

Adapted from the military sonar system which located enemy submarines during World War II, echosono-graphy is used to monitor almost half of all pregnancies and deliveries in the United States. It can determine the presence and location of one or more fetuses in their early stages, indicate a safe area for amniocentesis during the middle stages, and pinpoint the positions of head, umbilical cord and placenta just before birth.

Sonograms have also become an important diagnostic tool. Careful examination can reveal spinal and heart deformities as well as such telltale physical signals as the widely spaced eyes and the flattened pelvis usually associated with Down's syndrome.

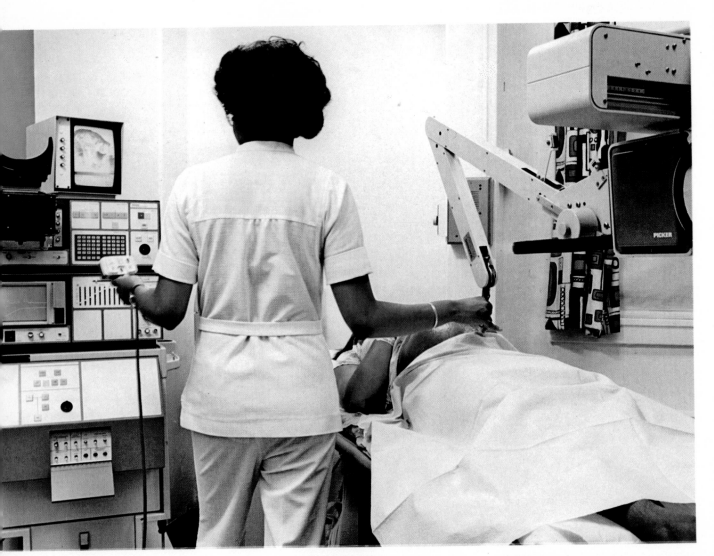

A REASSURING PEEK
A mature fetus appears on a display screen as a technician scans a pregnant woman's abdomen with an ultrasonic probe that transmits and receives about 1,000 high-frequency pulses per second. The device in the technician's left hand provides instant photographs to be studied by an obstetrician for delivery complications.

AN ULTRASONIC PORTRAIT
An 8-month-old fetus, one arm extending up inside the curve of its mother's belly, is outlined in this sonogram. The circular shape at bottom is the top of the skull, divided by the brain midline. Though sonograms are checked in black and white, this one was processed for easier reading by electronically turning tones into colors.

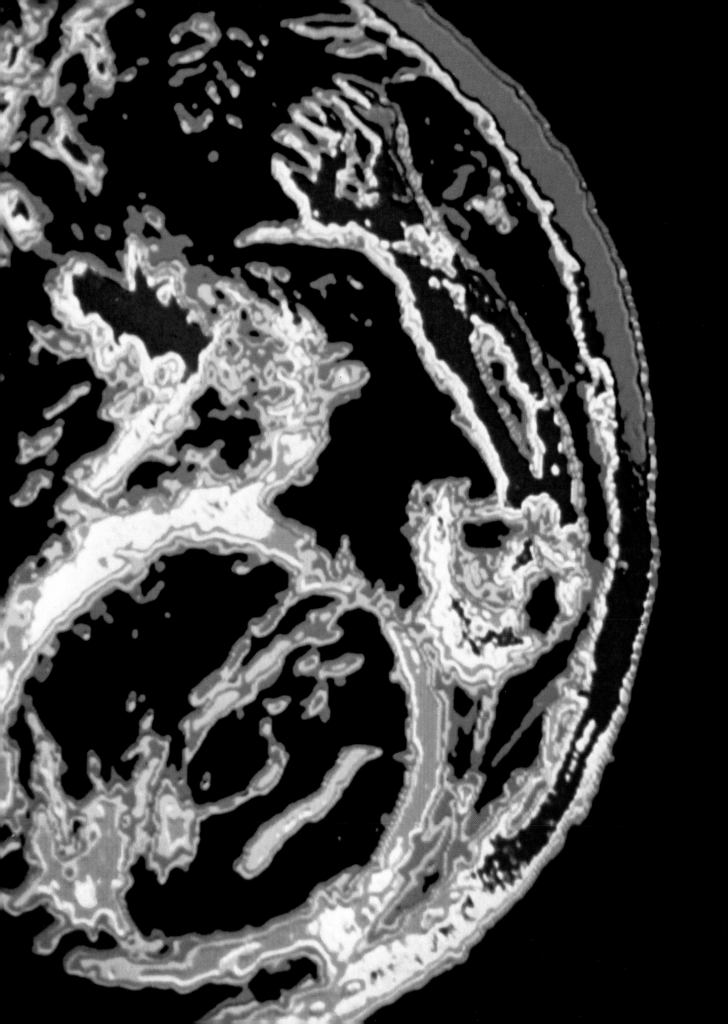

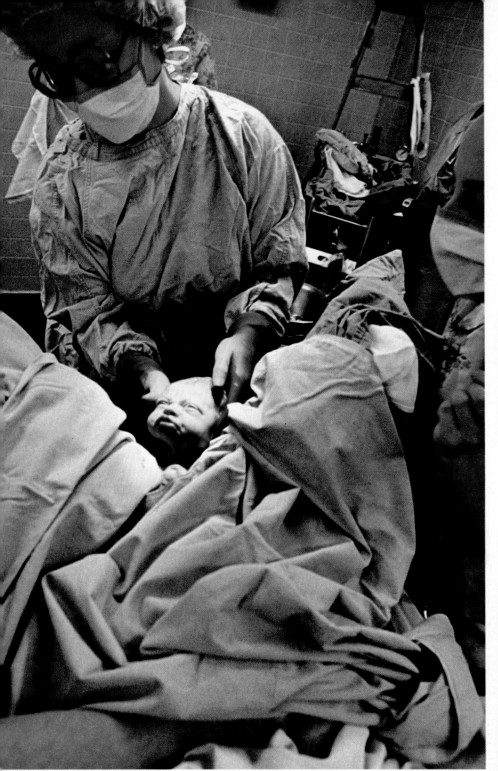

A TEST OF LUNG POWER
The newborn girl, her severed umbilical cord clamped shut, cries vigorously as she rests on her delighted mother's stomach. A baby's critical first cry, indicating that the respiratory system is functioning properly, is usually a spontaneous event, although a doctor may resort to a gentle spanking or a back rub to produce it.

The End and the Beginning

By the time that a full-term fetus is ready to be born, 266 days after conception, it has become a miniature human averaging 15 to 20 inches (38-50 cm) in length, and 6 to 8 pounds (3-4 kg) in weight, and is well prepared for its abrupt transition. In its final six weeks, the fetus doubles its weight, with much of the gain going into a temporary layer of fat that will provide warmth until the newborn adjusts to the lower temperatures of its new world. Its blood is fortified with maternal antibodies to provide protection until its own system of immunity becomes fully operative.

Most hospitals use a standard scoring system to determine a newborn infant's health. Point values of 0, 1 or 2 are assigned for responses to five key tests of heart rate, respiration, muscle tone, reflex irritability and color. A total score of 7 or more is considered good and 4 to 6 is fair, while 3 or below is poor. But with the assistance of modern medicine, many babies are able to match the score of the newborn girl shown here: a perfect 10.

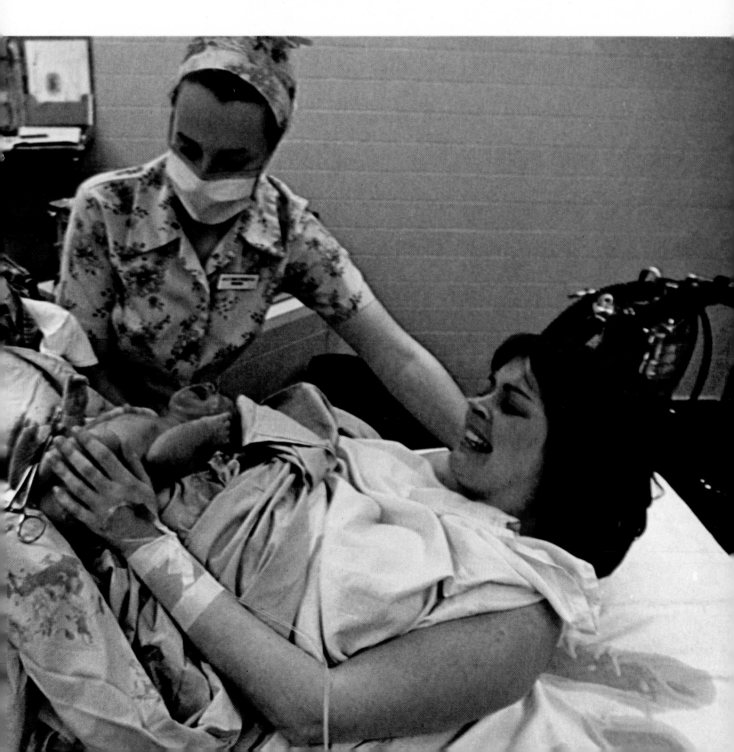

The Many Ways to Gauge the Body

Few objects have been as thoroughly scrutinized by modern science as the human body. It has been measured and weighed in all manner of ways; its capacities and functions have been calculated and evaluated in minute detail. Of the mountains of data which have been gradually accumulated, some of the items of most direct interest to the layman are reported on this and on the following two pages.

On page 194 is a map showing the life expectancy of men and women by countries and a table of the energy output of both sexes according to activity. And on page 195 is a chart of salient structural and physiological differences between the sexes. The table below lists the normal range and the known maximums and minimums of certain bodily measures and functions, along with some statistics on childbearing.

THE WIDE RANGE OF HUMAN STATISTICS

MEASURE	NORMAL	MAXIMUM	MINIMUM
HEIGHT	Men: 51''-79'' Women: 47''-73.5'' (varies with ethnic and regional groups)	The tallest man on record was Robert Wadlow of Illinois, who stood 107''. A victim of pituitary gigantism, he died at 22.	The shortest person on record was a 23.2-inch dwarf, Pauline Musters. Born in 1876, she died of pneumonia at the age of 19.
WEIGHT	Men: 112-204 lbs. Women: 92-173 lbs. (U.S.)	Robert Hughes of Illinois weighed 1,069 lbs. shortly before his death in 1958.	Lucia Zarate of Mexico weighed 4 lbs., 11 oz. at age 17. By the time she was 20, she weighed 13 lbs.
NUMBER OF HAIRS ON HEAD	120,000 (average)	Natural blondes can have as many as 140,000.	The minimum (excluding baldness) usually occurs among natural redheads, who can have as few as 90,000.
BODY TEMPERATURE	97-99°F.	At 110° F., fatal hemorrhages occur, and cells degenerate and die. Recovery from temperatures higher than 110° is extremely rare.	At 79.5°F., the heart fails. One rare exception was a girl who recovered from a low of 60.8°F.
HEART BEATS PER MINUTE	60-85 (at rest)	In young people, during strenuous exercise, the heart may beat as often as 270 times a minute.	50-60 (during sleep)
BLOOD PRESSURE	120/80 mm. (at age of 20)	A person with severe hypertension may develop pressure as high as 300/150—i.e., 300 mm. of pressure when the heart is contracted, 150 when relaxed.	Just after birth, pressure may be as low as 74/38.
SLEEP NEEDED PER DAY	7-9 hrs. (adults)	Newborn babies require 18 to 20 hrs. a day.	Oldsters may get along on as little as 5 hrs. a day.
SIZE OF BABIES AT BIRTH	7.3 lbs. (median)	The largest baby on record was a 24-lb., 4-oz. boy born in Turkey.	The smallest baby known to have survived was a 10-oz. girl born in the U.S. in 1938.
BIRTHS PER WOMAN (AGED 15-44)	2.4 (median, U.S.)	A Russian peasant woman gave birth to 69 children—16 sets of twins, 7 sets of triplets and 4 sets of quadruplets.	
CHILDBEARING AGE	25.4 (median, U.S.)	In 1956 a child was born to a 57-year-old Oregon woman.	In 1939 a child was born to a 5-year-old Peruvian Indian girl.

KEY: 1 ounce = 28 grams, 1 pound = 0.45 kilograms, 1 gallon = 3.8 liters, 1 quart = 0.95 liters, 1 inch = 2.54 centimeters, °Centigrade = (°Fahrenheit −32)/1.8

LIFE EXPECTANCIES AROUND THE WORLD

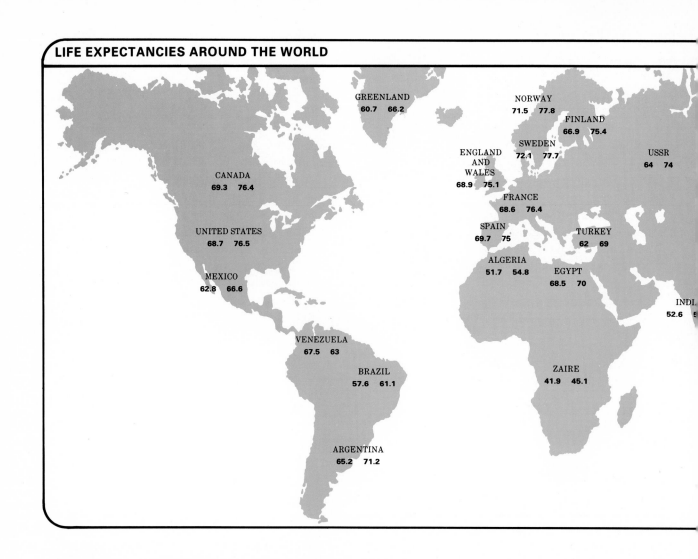

GREENLAND
60.7 66.2

NORWAY
71.5 77.8

FINLAND
66.9 75.4

SWEDEN
72.1 77.7

ENGLAND
AND
WALES
68.9 75.1

USSR
64 74

CANADA
69.3 76.4

FRANCE
68.6 76.4

SPAIN
69.7 75

TURKEY
62 69

UNITED STATES
68.7 76.5

ALGERIA
51.7 54.8

EGYPT
68.5 70

MEXICO
62.8 66.6

INDIA
52.6

VENEZUELA
67.5 63

BRAZIL
57.6 61.1

ZAIRE
41.9 45.1

ARGENTINA
65.2 71.2

THE ENERGY SPENT BY WOMEN AND MEN

WOMEN	KILOCALORIES	MEN	KILOCALORIES
LYING AT REST	.98	LYING AT REST	1.5
STANDING	1.11	STANDING	1.25
OFFICE WORK	1.31-1.72	OFFICE WORK	1.6
PEELING POTATOES	1.29	PEELING POTATOES	2.7
WASHING DISHES	1.53	WASHING DISHES	3.3
WASHING AND DRESSING	3.3	WASHING AND DRESSING	3.37
WALKING	2.9	WALKING	5.1
MAKING BEDS	5.4	MAKING BEDS	7
SKIING ON LEVEL HARD SNOW	10.8	SKIING ON LEVEL HARD SNOW	9.9

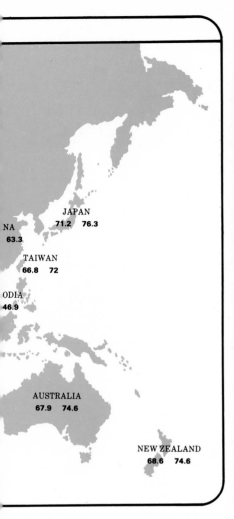

JAPAN
NA 71.2 76.3
63.3
TAIWAN
66.8 72
ODIA
46.9

AUSTRALIA
67.9 74.6

NEW ZEALAND
68.6 74.6

SOME DIFFERENCES BETWEEN THE SEXES

MEASURE	WOMEN	MEN
WEIGHT OF BRAIN		
Small	**37.04** ozs.	**38.8** ozs.
Average	**44.98** ozs.	**49.38** ozs.
Large	**54.68** ozs.	**60** ozs.
WEIGHT OF HEART	**9** ozs. **(255 g)**	**11** ozs. **(312 g)**
QUANTITY OF BLOOD	**1-1.25** gals.	**1.3-1.5** gals.
SURFACE AREA OF SKIN	**1.93** sq. yds.	**2.21** sq. yds.
WATER: % OF BODY WEIGHT	**54%**	**60%**
MUSCLE: % OF BODY WEIGHT	**36%**	**42%**
FAT: % OF BODY WEIGHT	**28%**	**18%**
BONE: % OF BODY WEIGHT	**18%**	**18%**
AVERAGE LENGTH OF SPINE	**24** ins.	**28** ins.
TOTAL LUNG CAPACITY AT AGE 25		
Small	**3.3** qts.	**4.5** qts.
Average	**4.4** qts.	**6.8** qts.
Large	**5.7** qts.	**9.5** qts.
NUMBER OF BREATHS PER MINUTE (AT REST)	**20-22**	**14-18**
INTAKE OF AIR PER BREATH		
Resting	**.36** qt.	**.79** qt.
Light work	**.91** qt.	**1.77** qts.
Heavy work	**.93** qt.	**2.15** qts.
Deepest possible intake (vital capacity) at age 25	**3.17** qts.	**5.18** qts.
NUMBER OF RED BLOOD CELLS PER CUBIC MILLIMETER (BLOOD COUNT)—U.S. AVERAGE	**4,000,000-5,000,000**	**4,300,000-5,700,000**

THE SPAN OF LIFE. Improved nutrition, medical care and hygiene have combined to create longer life expectancies almost everywhere in the world. *(map above).* For each country, life-expectancy figures at birth for males are shown at left, for females at right.

THE MEASURE OF ENERGY. The body uses two thirds of the energy it extracts from food for vital processes. This energy is gauged in calories, the heat-producing value of food. Some common pursuits and the energy they consume per minute are listed at left.

THE SCOPE OF VARIATION. Beyond observable distinctions between men and women, there are innumerable contrasts in both the composition of the body and the way it performs. Some of these, between healthy adults of the two sexes, are listed at right.

FURTHER READING

General

Asimov, Isaac, *The Human Body*. Houghton Mifflin Company, 1964.

Carlson, Anton J., Victor Johnson and H. Mead Cavert, *The Machinery of the Body*. The University of Chicago Press, 1961.

Eckstein, Gustav, *The Body Has a Head*. Harper & Row, 1970.

King, Barry G., and Mary Jane Showers, *Human Anatomy and Physiology*. W. B. Saunders, 1969.

Miller, Benjamin F., *The Complete Medical Guide*. Simon & Schuster, 1978.

Miller, Benjamin F., and Ruth Goode, *Man and His Body*. Simon & Schuster, 1960.

Van Amerongen, C., *The Way Things Work Book of the Body*. George Allen & Unwin, 1979.

History

Atkinson, Donald T., *Magic, Myth and Medicine*. Arno, 1974.

Bettmann, Otto C., *A Pictorial History of Medicine*. Charles C. Thomas, 1979.

Castiglioni, Arturo, *History of Medicine*. Aronson, 1973.

Lehrer, Steven, *Explorers of the Body*. Doubleday & Co., Inc., 1979.

Miller, Jonathan, *The Body in Question*. Random House, 1978.

Sigerist, Henry E., *The Great Doctors*. Arno, 1974.

Singer, Charles, *A Short History of Anatomy and Physiology from the Greeks to Harvey*. Dover Publications, Inc., 1957.

Special Subjects

Asimov, Isaac, *The Human Brain*. Houghton Mifflin Company, 1964.

Beaumont, William S., *Experiments and Observations on the Gastric Juice and Physiology of Digestion*. Scholarly, 1976.

Chewning, Emily Blair, and Dana Levy, *Anatomy Illustrated*. Simon & Schuster, 1979.

Dandy, Walter E., *The Brain*. Harper & Row, 1969.

Glasser, Ronald J., *The Body is the Hero*. Random House, 1976.

Greene, Raymond, *Human Hormones*. McGraw-Hill, 1970.

Kezdi, Paul, *You and Your Heart*. Atheneum, 1977.

Moore, Francis D., *Transplant: The Give and Take of Tissue Transplantation*. Simon & Schuster, 1972.

Phibbs, Brendan, *The Human Heart*. Mosby, 1979.

Rugh, Roberts, and Landrum B. Shettles, *From Conception to Birth: The Drama of Life's Beginnings*. Harper & Row, 1971.

Schlossberg, Leon, *The Johns Hopkins Atlas of Human Functional Anatomy*. Ed. by George D. Zuidema. The Johns Hopkins University Press, 1977.

Tanner, J. M., *Fetus into Man: Physical Growth from Conception to Maturity*. Harvard University Press, 1978.

Woodburne, Russell T., *Essentials of Human Anatomy*. Oxford University Press, 1973.

Wooldridge, Dean E., *The Machinery of the Brain*. McGraw-Hill, 1963.

ACKNOWLEDGMENTS

The editors of the revised edition are particularly indebted to Dr. Lawrence E. Hinkle Jr., Professor of Medicine at the New York Hospital-Cornell Medical Center; and to Dr. Jeffery L. Barker, National Institute of Neurological and Communicative Disorders and Stroke, National Institutes of Health, Bethesda, Maryland; Dr. Hans Frangenheim, Chefarzt der Städtischen Frauenklinik, Constance, Germany; Dr. Marilyn S. Horowitz, Associate Director, Blood Derivatives Program, New York Blood Center; Dr. Harold T. Meryman, Head, Cryobiology Laboratory, The American Red Cross, Bethesda, Maryland; Dr. Estelle R. Ramey, Professor of Physiology and Biophysics, Georgetown University School of Medicine; Dr. Melchior Savarese, Chief of Staff, Columbia Hospital for Women, Washington, D.C.; Dr. Harvey Schwartz, Assistant Clinical Professor of Medicine, Georgetown University School of Medicine; and Patrick C. Steptoe, Oldham, England.

Consulting editors for the first edition were René Dubos, Emeritus Professor of Pathology, The Rockefeller University, New York; Henry Margenau, Eugene Higgins Professor of Physics and Natural Philosophy Emeritus, Yale University, New Haven; and the late C. P. Snow, the novelist and Fellow of Christ's College, Cambridge University, Cambridge, England.

The editors of the first edition of this book are indebted to the following persons and institutions who helped in the preparation of the book: Norman Budde, American Medical Association; Dr. Farrington Daniels, Associate Professor of Medicine, New York Hospital-Cornell Medical Center; Dr. Gustave J. Dammin, Pathologist-in-Chief, Peter Bent Brigham Hospital, Boston; Dartmouth College; William DeLay, Director of Public Relations, American Academy of General Practice, Kansas City, Missouri; Dr. Ivan Dunaief, Kings County Hospital, Brooklyn; Dr. Douglas C. Eaglesham, Director, Department of Radiology, Guelph General Hospital, Ontario, Canada; Dr. Ralph L. Engle Jr., Associate Professor of Medicine, New York Hospital-Cornell Medical Center; Essex County Medical Society, East Orange, New Jersey; Dr. Henry Fischer, Assistant Curator, Egyptian Collection, Metropolitan Museum of Art; Dr. Donald H. Ford, Associate Professor of Anatomy, State University of New York, Downstate Medical Center,

Brooklyn; Dr. Wilbur D. Hagamen Jr., Associate Professor of Anatomy, New York Hospital-Cornell Medical Center; Dr. Sami Hashim, Director, Laboratory of Metabolic and Nutritional Research, Saint Luke's Hospital, New York City; Dr. James G. Hirsch, Associate Professor of Medicine and Microbiology, The Rockefeller University, New York City; Dr. Allan E. Inglis, Hospital for Special Surgery, New York City; Roy Keaton, Director, Magazine Relations, American Medical Association; Frederick Kilgour, Librarian, Yale Medical Library, Yale University; Dr. Hymen S. Mayerson, Chairman, Department of Physiology, Tulane University School of Medicine; Dr. Richard Manegold, American Medical Association; The Massachusetts General Hospital; Dr. Edmund McNally, Chief of Gastroenterology, Kings County Hospital, Brooklyn; Dr. Ade T. Milhorat, Director, Institute for Muscle Disease, New York City; Dr. Charles R. Noback, Professor of Anatomy, College of Physicians and Surgeons, Columbia University; Oberlin College; Dr. Carl Pfaffmann, Department of Psychology, Brown University; Duncan M. Potter Jr., General Manager, Special Instruments Laboratory, Inc., Knoxville; Presbyterian-Saint Luke's Hospital, Chicago; E. F. Richner, Manager, News Services, Public Relations Dept., Eastman Kodak Company, Rochester, New York; Dr. Alfred A. Rosenthal, New York City; Dr. Albert L. Rubin, Associate Professor of Medicine, New York Hospital-Cornell Medical Center; Dr. Alexander Sandow, Chief, Division of Physiology, Institute for Muscle Disease, New York City; Sinai Hospital of Baltimore; Loren B. Sjöström, Arthur D. Little, Inc., Cambridge, Massachusetts; Leon Summit, Editor, *Spectrum*, Charles Pfizer and Co., Inc., New York City; Dr. Roy Swan, Professor (Chairman) of Anatomy, New York Hospital-Cornell Medical Center; Beverley Tarlov, New York Hospital-Cornell Medical Center; Dr. David D. Thompson, Associate Professor of Medicine, New York Hospital-Cornell Medical Center; Dorothy S. Ullmann, New York Hospital-Cornell Medical Center; University of Illinois College of Medicine, Chicago; Alice D. Weaver, and librarians of the Rare Book Department, The New York Academy of Medicine; Alfred F. Zobel, Director of Public Relations, Hoffmann-La Roche, Inc., Nutley, New Jersey.

INDEX

Numerals in italics indicate a photograph or painting of the subject mentioned.

PICTURE CREDITS

The sources for the illustrations that appear in this book are shown below. Credits for pictures from left to right are separated by commas, from top to bottom by dashes.

Cover—Lee Boltin

CHAPTER 1: 8—Bob Landry. 10, 11—Drawings by Nicholas Fasciano. 12—Bottom, Derek Bayes. 13—The Bettmann Archive. 15—Derek Bayes. 17—Eric Schaal courtesy Yale University Medical Library. 18, 19—H. Lund Hans courtesy Danish National Museum, Hamburg Museum Für Völkerkunde—J. R. Eyerman courtesy Museum of Man, San Diego. 20—Courtesy Roemer-Pelizaeus Museum, Hildesheim, Germany. 21—Khamis Abdel Latif courtesy Cairo Museum, Henry Groskinsky courtesy the Metropolitan Museum of Art, Rogers Fund, 1929. 22—Emmett Bright courtesy Naples National Museum. 23—Aldo Durazzi courtesy Piacenza City Museum—Derek Bayes courtesy British Museum. 24—Bodleian Library, Oxford. 25—Bodleian Library, Oxford, except top: Khamis Abdel Latif courtesy Museum of Islamic Arts, Cairo. 26, 27—Giraudon courtesy Condé Art Museum, Chantilly, France. 28—Courtesy British Museum, Vatican Library. 29—The Pierpont Morgan Library. 30, 31—Courtesy British Museum. 32, 33—Color by Fritz Kredel of Vesalius drawings courtesy University of Padua Library.

CHAPTER 2: 34—Robert W. Kelley. 36, 37—Drawings by Nicholas Fasciano. 38—Drawings by George Schwenk. 40—Drawings by George Schwenk. 41—Drawing by Charles Gottlieb. 43—Drawings by Elliot Herman and Paul Calle. 44, 45—Drawings by Elliot Herman and Paul Davis. 46 through 53—Drawings by Elliot Herman and Paul Calle.

CHAPTER 3: 54—Bob Gomel for *Sports Illustrated.* 56—Drawing by Adolph E. Brotman and Charles Mikolaycak. 57—The Bettmann Archive. 58, 59, 60—Drawings by Richard Boland. 62—Drawing by Mark A. Binn. 63—Drawing by Joe Lambandero adapted from illustration by Professor D. Denny-Brown in *Reflex Activity of the Spinal Cord,* Oxford University Press. 65—Andreas Feininger. 66—Courtesy Bethlehem Steel Co. 67—Gjon Mili. 68, 69—Top, Andreas Feininger; bottom, G. Gheradi-A. Fiorelli. 70, 71—Andreas Feininger, Carl Iwasaki. 72—Gjon Mili. 74—Oscar Savio. 75—Gjon Mili.

CHAPTER 4: 76—George Silk. 78—Eric Schaal courtesy Academy of Medicine. 79—Drawing by Adolph E. Brotman. 80—Drawing by Otto van Eersel. 82—Drawings by Nicholas Fasciano adapted from illustration by Bunji Tagawa in *Scientific American.* 84—The Bettmann Archive. 87, 88—Fritz Goro. 89—Don Wong from Photo Researchers, Inc.—Dr. Judith Hardy Stashin. 90, 91—PIP-ZFA. 92—Dr. G. Douglas Talbott—Dr. James Hirsch. 93—Dr. James Hirsch. 94—Cutter Laboratories, Inc. 95—Cathie Schilling courtesy New York Blood Center. 96—Greg MacGregor courtesy New York Blood Center—Courtesy Haemonetics Corporation. 97—Courtesy Massachusetts General Hospital.

CHAPTER 5: 98—Alfred Eisenstaedt. 100—Drawing by Joe Lambandero. 101—Drawing by Nicholas Fasciano. 103—Drawing by Nicholas Fasciano. 104, 105—Drawings by Otto van Eersel. 106—Eric Schaal courtesy Yale University. 109 through 117—Drawings by Push Pin Studio.

CHAPTER 6: 118—Monte Casazza. 121—Drawing by Otto van Eersel. 122—Drawings by Charles Mikolaycak. 124, 125—Drawings by George V. Kelvin. 127—Lee Johnson. 128, 129—Drawing by Victor Taylor, Bob Walsh. 130, 131—Courtesy St. Barnabas Medical Center. 132—Bill Auth courtesy Georgetown University Medical Center. 133—Courtesy Dr. Gustave J. Dammin, Peter Bent Brigham Hospital, Boston—Drawing by Victor Taylor. 134—Drawing by R. M. Chapin Jr. for *Time.* 135—Dr. John Retan. 136—Bill Ray for *The Changing Challenge*—courtesy UCLA School of Medicine. 137—Owen (S.K.) from Black Star. 138—Gordon Tenney. 139—Fritz Goro.

CHAPTER 7: 140—Sam Nocella. 142—Drawings by George Schwenk. 144—Drawing by Adolph E. Brotman. 145—Drawing by George V. Kelvin. 147—Drawings by Otto van Eersel. 148, 149—Drawings by Nicholas Fasciano. 151—Norman Snyder. 152—Drawing by Jack J. Kunz—drawing by Lowell Hess. 153—Ralph Morse. 154—Drawing by Jack J. Kunz—drawing by Lowell Hess. 155—Wayne Miller from Magnum. 156—Drawing by Jack J. Kunz—drawing by Lowell Hess. 157—Edward Clark. 158—Drawing by Caroll Jones—drawing by Lowell Hess. 159—A. Y. Owen. 160—Drawing by Caroll Jones—drawing by Lowell Hess. 161—Carroll Seghers II. 162—Ronny Jaques from Photo Researchers, Inc. 163—George Karger from PIX. 164, 165—Brian Seed from Black Star, Lee Johnson. 166, 167—John Launois from Black Star, Nina Leen.

CHAPTER 8: 168—By gracious permission of H. M. Queen Elizabeth II, Royal Collection, Crown Copyright Reserved; photograph Dr. Heinz Zinram. 170—Drawing by Nicholas Fasciano. 171—Museum of the City of New York. 172—Drawings by George V. Kelvin. 174, 175, 176, 177—Drawings by Adolph E. Brotman. 179—Tom Tracy. 180—Courtesy Dr. Hans Frangenheim, Chefarzt der Städtischen Frauenklinik, Constance, Germany. 181—Drawing by Nicholas Fasciano. 182, 183—Courtesy P. C. Steptoe, Oldham, England, and R. G. Edwards, Cambridge, England. 184, 185—Courtesy Dr. Hans Frangenheim, Chefarzt der Städtischen Frauenklinik, Constance, Germany. 186—© William Hubbell from Woodfin Camp & Assoc. 187, 188—John Neubauer. 189—© Howard Sochurek from Woodfin Camp & Assoc. 190, 191—Tom McClellan. 194, 195—Map by Nicholas Fasciano.

Printed in U.S.A.